50%
weight lost

100%
healthier

Then

I dedicate this book to all the strong women in my life, especially my mum and my sister. And to my husband, Rodney, who has always believed in me, and my son, Ethan.

Now

weightwatchers
reimagined

50%
weight lost

100%
healthier

Anna Van Dyken

Pan Macmillan Australia

Contents

What's that symbol?

Our guide to finding the best recipes for your dietary needs

 Gluten free Recipes with this symbol don't contain any gluten. Check the ingredients list of all packaged foods to be sure, and take care with cross-contamination.

 Dairy free Recipes with this symbol are free from all dairy products or use dairy-free substitutes.

 Vegetarian Recipes with this symbol don't contain meat or fish but may have dairy products or eggs.

 Vegan Recipes with this symbol don't contain any animal products, including meat, dairy, eggs and other animal-derived substances.

 Nut free Recipes with this symbol don't contain any nuts or nut-based products. Check the ingredients list of all packaged food to be sure, and take care with cross-contamination.

Welcome to WW

From humble beginnings setting up in a New York apartment, to becoming the world's leading sustainable weight-loss program with more than five million members, WW (formerly known as Weight Watchers) has come a long way since it all started over 57 years ago, evolving from one woman's inspiring success story to that of many.

Where it all began

Jean Nidetch, the company founder, had been overweight most of her life. She had become discouraged by years of fad dieting, having tried pills, hypnosis, and numerous quick-fix approaches, all of which led to regained weight. She decided to seek medically backed guidance instead, and entered a free 10-week weight-loss program sponsored by the New York City Board of Health's obesity clinic. The program was called the 'Prudent Diet' where she lost 9 kg, but her motivation waned with the lack of peer support she received during the program. This is when Jean's weekly meetings with her own support group began, and the seed for Weight Watchers was planted.

Jean began her own weight-loss support group by inviting some of her friends to her home once a week to discuss their goals, tips and challenges for weight-loss success. As word spread and attendee numbers grew, she finally launched Weight Watchers Inc. in May 1963. The first official meeting, held in a rented loft above a movie theatre in Queens, New York, attracted over 400 attendees. The winning formula of Weight Watchers quickly spread across the world and to Australia in 1969, holding the first meeting in Sydney.

50% **Weight Lost** | 100% **Healthier**

What we do today

In 2018, Weight Watchers became WW, reflecting our evolution into what we are today: a wellness company powered by the world's leading sustainable weight-loss program.

Having constantly evolved in line with the latest science and member needs, we've stood the test of time, delivering a trusted and sustainable program that remains a category leader both in Australia and across the globe. WW has retained the number 1 spot for weight loss for ten consecutive years, as judged by an independent panel of experts in the US News & World Report. It's also backed by over 100 clinical studies showing the program works, and is supported by even more incredible member success stories like Anna Van Dyken's.

At WW, our purpose is to inspire healthy habits for real life. For people, families, communities, the world – for everyone. While supporting members across Australia and New Zealand at hundreds of physical locations and through virtual workshops, we have also built a digital experience centred on the award-winning WW app that allows people to learn healthy habits their way, making our program accessible to all.

In addition to food, fitness, sleep and water tracking, the WW app is constantly developing and now includes everything from recipes and 24/7 WW Coach support, to a barcode scanner, meditations and workouts, providing holistic support across food, movement and mindset.

Community at our core

Community remains at the heart of our philosophy and it is this community that differentiates us. Our network of coaches, ambassadors and members live our purpose daily, encouraging and supporting each other through our community platforms to pay forward the techniques and success they've achieved with others. We are incredibly proud of our members' achievements and even more so of their ability to make these changes lasting and sustainable. We hope Anna's amazing story is a source of hope and help to you. Her inspiring collection of recipes deliver simple, delicious food that makes the journey that much easier and enjoyable too.

How *myWW* works today

The new program from WW is now customised to your needs, making losing weight easier than ever! Using a personal assessment in the WW app, *myWW* leverages details about your food preferences and lifestyle to match you to one of three food plans that best suits you – Green, Blue or Purple.

SmartPoints

On all three plans, every food and drink is assigned a SmartPoints value based on kilojoules, saturated fat, protein and sugar. You're given a daily SmartPoints budget based on your age, sex, weight and height, and can choose to spend it on any foods or drinks you like (which means you don't have to say no to a glass of wine with dinner or a chocolate treat occassionally!). As always, no food is off-limits on WW, so you don't need to miss out on the foods you love.

ZeroPoint foods

There's also an extensive list of ZeroPoint foods on every plan, containing options which form the foundation of a healthy eating pattern, and don't need to be measured or tracked. Depending on which plan you follow, these foods range from fruits and vegetables through to seafood, skinless chicken breast and even wholegrain pasta.

PART ONE

My Story

My story

When I was a little girl, I remember my grandmother said to me, 'You don't need a lot of ingredients to make good food tasty, you just need fresh food and a few things in the pantry.'

I still live by these wise words. You see, my grandparents Nonna and Nonno came from a generation where you made do with what you had, and that wasn't always much. Their backyard was a magical place where Nonno grew almost everything through each season, as they had been taught to do from generations past.

I would help my grandfather pick the delicious fruits, herbs and vegetables. Once we took all our treasures back inside, I would watch my grandmother transform the fresh food into family feasts. To this day, one of my favourite dishes is her cucumber and tomato salad sprinkled with oregano and drizzled with olive oil – simple food, tasting of summer. As the weather turned colder, Nonna would slow-cook broad beans, peas and tomatoes into the most amazing stew to be served with lamb.

We also kept chickens in the backyard and it was my job to collect the eggs. These made the best-ever frittatas using only three ingredients: eggs, onion and potato. And there was often the magical smell of homemade chicken soup cooking on the stove; it would waft from the kitchen filling the whole house and even make its way outside where I played. It always made me feel comforted and warm. A bowl of Nonna's chicken soup was like eating a bowl of love. We had it often, and when we were sick, it was Nonna's medicine and instantly made me feel better. Even now, whenever I get a cold or feel unwell, the first thing I reach for is chicken soup.

Such memories are not only vivid in my mind but also etched in my soul as reminders of my Italian heritage. In the kitchen, I was always helping Nonna, listening to her advice on how to mix the dough for the pasta to get the right feel, and taking it in turns kneading and shaping it, or being entrusted with the secret ingredient needed to make her famous ricotta cake. I have countless memories of the two of us together in the kitchen, me learning from her at her elbow,

watching, eating and enjoying life. Every day after school, I looked forward to getting home and enjoying afternoon tea with Nonna, which was always a sandwich with Italian cold meats, fruit and a sweet treat with a cold drink. My younger days were spent mainly with adults until my sister, Christina, was born when I was six.

As my nonna aged and I became an adult, she started to cook less and less, and eventually she went to live with my aunty. But she would often come and stay with me for a few days at a time, and just as I had watched her in the kitchen as a child, it felt like life had come full-circle as I cooked for her. I remembered all the foods she used to make us and tried to replicate them to make her happy and proud of me. My grandmother was not just my nonna; she was also like my second mother, my teacher and my friend. Everything I know about cooking came from her – the passion, the love of family and the generosity of sharing with others. I will always be grateful to her for everything she taught me, right up until the day she took her last breath.

Connecting food with comfort

My nonna fed her family with love, and this connection with food was passed on not only to me, but to other family members as well. In turn, I passed this 'traditional love' on to my own family, but now I wonder whether we might be at risk of showing too much love through food. The mentality was that the more we cooked for others, the more love we shared. We were completely unaware that it might be doing us harm as we never learned any self-control around food. Throughout my life, my love of food has always been intensely emotional – the strongest emotion is love, but

Clockwise from top left:
Me, aged two, with Mum at my
great-grandmother's house;
Rodney and me on our wedding
day; my grandmother making
pasta with my great-grandmother,
grandfather and mum; a recipe
handwritten by my grandmother
and passed down to me.

there can be sadness and grief in there, too. Using food for comfort, rather than nourishment, became a problem that I didn't even realise was developing. Taste was a big thing as well. If it was good, I didn't want it to stop; I wanted to keep eating more and more of it until there was no more to eat. Back then I didn't consider portion sizes; I just ate until I was 'full'. And even though my stomach may have been full, I always pushed beyond it. I had no off switch.

This problem continued throughout my childhood until my late teens, when I was a regular at the drive-throughs of fast-food outlets. And it was at this point where the really big weight gains began. At the time it seemed convenient to grab takeaway while out with friends or working during the week – they were easy choices. I knew I was getting bigger, but I didn't know how to control myself around foods I loved, and I did have a real hankering for burgers, fries and fried chicken. I didn't want to be fat, but I didn't want to give up all the foods I loved either.

By this time it seemed too hard to try and lose weight, so I didn't bother. I didn't think I would ever have a boyfriend because of my size, and as my lack of self-esteem and confidence plummeted I ate even more to comfort myself. I had no idea how much I weighed as I was too scared to step on any scales, so I lived in ignorance well past my teens.

I did make a few attempts in my twenties to switch to healthier options, but I really didn't know what I was doing. I tried to eat more salads, and have smaller portions; I tried restrictive dieting by cutting out fast food and carbs, but nothing lasted long, and, ultimately, it only made me binge eat.

I was still living at home at this time and I fell in love with baking, as did my sister, Christina. As we grew up, we became incredibly close. We spent most of our time together: shopping, watching our favourite shows and, of course, cooking. We would spend our weekends having bake-offs to see who could make the best cakes, slices, biscuits and pastries, both savoury and sweet. Chris and I enjoyed the fruits of our labours and, wanting to impress Mum, we got better and better at baking, and my weight kept increasing. (It didn't help that Chris hadn't any weight problem whatsoever.)

> **66**
> **Using food for comfort, rather than nourishment, became a problem."**

Bittersweet years

My first serious attempt at losing any real weight came at the age of twenty-seven, after I met my then (and only ever) boyfriend, Rodney. He asked me to marry him; I said yes – and I wanted to look good for my wedding.

One night, I saw a weight-loss advert on television that talked about eating real food, not pre-packaged food, and included going to a support group to learn how to lose weight. I chatted to Rod about it, saying I wanted to lose a bit of weight before the wedding, and he did too, so we gave it a go. It was the first time we ever went to Weight Watchers (as it was known then). It was also the first time I had stepped on the scales in years. I discovered that I weighed just over 100 kilos.

Together, we went on the WW program and within a few months I was down to 85 kilos – the smallest I had been in a very long time, and Rod had lost 10 or so kilos. The program worked well for us, and our wedding photos were gorgeous.

Married life was blissful and full of lavish meals to impress my new husband. I introduced Rod to my world of Italian cuisine, re-creating the dishes I grew up with and still loved. Cheesy pasta and pizza were regulars on the menu, as were Italian meats that Rod had never eaten before. I baked sweet treats such as chocolate cakes and buttery biscuits, and we ate homemade bread served warm with thick butter.

It didn't take long before the weight came back on.

> ## 66
> **Even as I sit and write this, I wipe away the tears."**

The year before I met Rodney, my darling Christina had been diagnosed with osteosarcoma, a rare type of bone cancer. She was just eighteen. Her cancer was terminal, although I wasn't to find that out until much later.

After Rod and I got married, Chris went into her first remission (at the age of twenty-three), but her cancer soon returned. She lived only a street away from me with her boyfriend who cared for her, and so we spent even more time together. My parents lived really close by as well, and my grandparents were only a few minutes further away. We all lived in walking distance of each other and, perhaps because of that, we indulged more than ever.

I often made Chris her favourite meal, one that our nonna used to make for us. It was pasta with peas, but almost like a soup. She asked for it specifically while she was in hospital, and of course I made it with love, hoping that she could keep it down; sometimes it was all she looked forward to. I also made her brownies and other sweet treats and although she wanted to eat them, mostly she couldn't.

Her chemo sessions were gruelling and painful, and watching her suffer took its toll on all of us. Her battle was six years long. She went through three short periods of remission, but each time the cancer came back more aggressively until eventually it spread to her lung.

It seemed so unfair. She was so very young and hadn't even really started living her life yet. She was, however, always positive, always smiling and never whinging or letting things get her down – well, not in front of us anyway.

Chris was such a strong, brave girl, and her illness made all my weight issues seem so irrelevant; the only thing we wanted to focus on was living each day happily.

Naively, I thought that she was going to be okay, that she would beat the cancer and go on to live a happy, healthy life, getting married as I had, and beginning her own family. I had this image in my head that all our children would grow up together, that we would celebrate birthdays and outings, keep our Sunday pasta day and enjoy every Christmas as one big happy family.

It was not to be. Chris died at the age of twenty-four on 19 January 2001.

My life was beyond shattered. We were the best of friends, not just sisters. We always had each other and relied on each other; she was everything to me. I helped look after her when she was young, and I looked out for her as we grew up – that's what big sisters were for – but I couldn't save her from this. For me, the best years of my life were shared with her and now she was gone.

Even as I sit and write this, I wipe away the tears.

The weeks following her death were hard, in fact the hardest of my life. The truth is I didn't know how I was going to go on. And then in March, just before Easter, Rodney and I learned I was pregnant.

To this day, I think that Chris sent down that gift to help us heal, and to give me what I had longed for: a child. I've held on to that thought tightly ever since and I am forever grateful for such a prize.

I believe finding out that I had this tiny life growing inside me stopped me from grieving. I didn't want my baby to feel the pain and hurt that I had inside. Crying for days at a time and spiralling into depression was something I wanted to avoid, so I buried the grief throughout my pregnancy and ate to comfort myself instead.

Ethan was born the same year, in December, just before Christmas. He was the light of my life and he still is. It was bittersweet to have him as Chris would have loved him so very much.

In the months after Ethan's birth, once again I turned to food, and this is where my weight got completely out of control. I didn't care about myself anymore. My health came last – all I wanted was comfort.

The day that changed our lives

The years passed and I stayed at home to raise Ethan and, in the way I had also been shown, I gave him all the love in the world through my attention – and my food. I made him things that I had eaten as a child: pasta with cheese (his favourite, just like his mum), ice cream, homemade bread and sweets. I spoiled him with treats to make up for the things I couldn't do with him. It was fun to be in the kitchen together baking cupcakes and eating them, and seeing the shine on Ethan's face as I handed him one.

Looking back now, of course it was an echo of all the good times I had in the kitchen with Chris. I wanted to extend that feeling with Ethan. Somehow it made Chris a part of our day; I would eat a cake for me *and* for her.

The kitchen and dinner table are two spaces that make up the heart of the home. There, the love of two worlds collide – the love of family and the love of cooking for them. Preparing meals was (and still is) so important to me, and sitting together and eating as a family reminded me of my childhood and what I wanted for my own family.

I wanted Ethan to feel what I had felt at the dinner table when my nonna or mum put a plate of food in front of me they'd so lovingly prepared, knowing how much I would love eating it. It made them feel happy that I was happy, and I wanted that for both Rod and Ethan.

At this stage, I was a size 28 to size 30. When Ethan was two years old, we moved to a house directly across the road from a park in the hope of using it as he got older, but it never happened. I was so big my size stopped me from taking him across the road; it stopped me from getting down on the floor and playing with him, as I couldn't get back up or would need help if I did. Instead, I sat on the couch and sat him in front of me to watch him play. In order to interact, I had to put him next to me on the couch, or play at the kitchen table.

By the time Ethan started primary school, especially between years 2 through to 5, I knew we were all slowly getting fatter, but failed to fully recognise the problem.

There's no question that much of the reason for this was me trying to fill the void of not having my sister in our lives. Rodney and I talked about her often, we cried often, we laughed often and we ate a lot more often, too. Ethan knew exactly who she was as he was growing up, which was so important to me.

It wasn't until 2012, when he was in year 5 at school, that issues arose with Ethan's weight. By the age of ten, he was being teased about being what I would call 'chubby'. He was pretty tall for his age and carried his weight well, but I had never actually weighed him. It was only later on that we learned he was being bullied for being the biggest boy in the class.

Little did I realise back then that one day at Ethan's school would change all our lives.

That day, Ethan's PE class had its annual cross-country race where the kids had to run around the school block, then do a final lap of the school oval before crossing the finish line and sitting down. I remember all the other parents standing there, cheering their children on as they streamed toward the finish line, one by one. There were 30 in the class. Twenty-nine of them crossed the line, but not Ethan.

I began to panic slightly: he was asthmatic and, not knowing where he was, I feared something awful had happened. Finally, he appeared, huffing and puffing from around the corner. I felt such relief, sadness and concern that it had taken him so long to finish. The PE teacher made Ethan do that final lap of the oval, sending out two kids who had already finished to accompany him, with all his classmates and their parents watching.

Tears welled up in my eyes as I saw him struggling, and I felt his humiliation. As he crossed the finish line, I tried to hold back my emotions as he stared straight into my eyes, his face flushed red, trying to catch his breath. 'Mum,' he gasped, 'don't you EVER make me do that again.'

In that very moment I knew I had to act.

It was only later that I discovered my ten-year-old son weighed almost 80 kilos. I was morbidly obese. And that very same week my husband was diagnosed with type 2 diabetes. It was a perfect storm. I *had* to change my family's unhealthy lifestyle. This was my responsibility. How had I let us all get to the point where our health was so poor?

As a family we had stopped doing so many things together that most people take for granted. We weren't

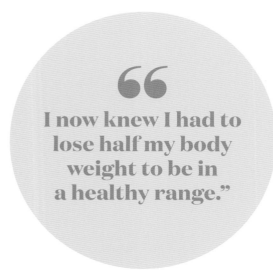

> "
> I now knew I had to lose half my body weight to be in a healthy range."

doing little things like going to the movies or out to dinner because I couldn't fit in the chairs anymore – I was too big – and going on a picnic was out because I couldn't sit on the ground; and taking Ethan to the park never happened because it was hard to move and I would tire easily. It was so selfish of me that my family had to miss out because of my weight. And then my doctor told me that if I continued on the unhealthy path I was on, I wouldn't see the age of sixty.

I decided I wanted to live for my son and husband.

Little by little

Four days later, at 9am on a Saturday morning, I walked into my local WW meeting. We'd had success before with WW and I wanted to give it another go. This time, I went with a bigger purpose.

There was a long line of about fifteen women there that morning. I scoured the room and quickly realised I was the largest person there. My heart sank as the dread of having to face the scales loomed. I was embarrassed and ashamed at being so big. It was so confronting to step on the scales for the first time in years and see the number that stared back at me. I was almost 143 kilos.

The overwhelming reality hit me hard, but I knew I was there not just for me, but also for my son and my husband. I was there to learn how to change the habits that had become part of my everyday life over the years.

I went home armed with the tools I needed to help bring about such change: kitchen scales, cookbooks, measuring spoons and downsized plates. With positive attitudes, we sat down as a family that night and talked about how making some changes would improve our health.

As parents, we didn't want to encourage a 'diet' mentality; after all, Ethan was still a child, and depriving him, or any of us, of foods we loved was not what we wanted or needed. We wanted to incorporate all foods into our lifestyle but learn how to control portions. That was the major reason I chose to attend meetings. I already knew how to cook; I just needed to learn a different way of cooking, to make it healthier.

We let Ethan choose the recipes from the WW cookbooks so he would be more willing to try new meals, and Rod was completely supportive right from the start. Both Ethan and Rodney began weighing themselves at home: for Rodney, this was weekly; for Ethan, monthly, as we didn't want the scales to be the only way to measure progress or success. They both needed a starting point, just as I did, to keep track of how we were all going.

I remember sitting in our bedroom one night within a week of starting and sobbing, feeling so overwhelmed by how I was going to accomplish my own weight loss. I now knew I had to lose half my body weight to be in a healthy range. HALF MY BODY WEIGHT! How on earth was I going to do that?

Then Rod walked in and asked me what was wrong. I was truly scared, and I told him so. He looked at me and said, 'You can't change everything at once. You need to do things little by little. We have to lose a lot of weight, so let's break it down into smaller goals. That way it won't be as daunting.' Those wise words completely changed my attitude.

As the first two weeks passed, I decided to change one habit at a time, and then aim for smaller, achievable 5-kilo goals. My focus, however, was always on Ethan, and showing him how to make small changes each week. This was when I started to make 'snack boxes' for him to take to school, so he had a variety of things to choose from each day. We made them together the night before. Because I wanted this to be a fun learning experience for him, he decided what he wanted. This helped to steer him towards his own healthier choices. Later, I incorporated snack boxes into my and Rod's daily food intake as well.

Clockwise from top left: Me, Rod and Ethan, aged four, at my cousin's wedding; at my heaviest weight of 142 kilos; me and my bridesmaids: my sister Christina (left) and my best friend of 30 years, Donna; me, Ethan, aged ten, and Rodney, at our heaviest.

Clockwise from top left: dressed up for the 2013 WW gala; with my WW coach Andrea Walsh in 2017, on the day I reached my goal weight; at the WW magazine photoshoot, feeling beautiful for the first time in my life; three years at my goal weight and still walking every day; Ethan and Rod in 2013, having reached their healthy weight range.

I knew it wasn't fair that we couldn't go to restaurants because of me, so I decided that instead of going out, I would bring the restaurant home to us. I took more care preparing our meals, making them restaurant quality and plating the meals as a chef would. I know we eat with our eyes first and so I was keen to make the food look as delicious as possible. For me, that was always the best part of going out to eat – that moment of *wow!* So I worked on capturing that *wow!* moment at home. I committed to doing this for every single meal. Now this is something I just do.

And Friday nights became movie nights at home, though I made healthier portions of movie snacks. I also made smart swaps, choosing healthier low-fat, low-sugar alternatives when planning my shopping lists. We learned what a portion size looked like (considerably less than I had been used to) from following the recipes in the WW cookbooks and seeing the photographs. We still ate ice cream on special occasions, but we learned the difference between treats and everyday foods from following the basics of the program.

Perseverance – and tears of pride

It's funny how life can play out. About a month after I started at WW, our small business went into voluntary bankruptcy. We lost everything we owned: our house, our cars and all our savings. We were devastated and at a crossroads. I wondered how we were going to survive, and how we could start over again.

The first thing I thought I would need to cut was the cost of WW meetings, but Rod made his thoughts quite clear: 'You can't put a price on your health. Without you, there is no family, and that is worth more than all the money in the world. We will find the funds, and you will keep going to help us all.' So I persevered, now more determined than ever not to let myself or my family down.

Once I got the hang of the program, I began experimenting with my own recipes and adjusting meals that I had grown up with, and still loved, into healthier, WW-friendly versions. One morning I asked Rod what he would like for dinner. His response was, 'You know that rice dish you did last week? That was nice. Can you make it again?' I had no clue which

> **66**
> **I was more determined than ever not to let myself or my family down."**

meal he was talking about because I had cooked so many by then. He picked up on my confusion and suggested that next time I made a new recipe, I wrote it down, adding, 'That way you know which one I mean!'

Well, that made sense to me. However, I decided to go one step further and document not only the recipe, but also attach a photo of it for reference, using a new app I had discovered called Instagram. This would become a personal food journal, and document not just my recipes but my journey as well, in order for me to keep track of my progress.

At first, I had concentrated on the food and getting that right, and now we ventured into the arena of physical exercise. Initially, the most I could do was walk to the letterbox and back. That was hard and tired me out quickly, but I worked on it alone in addition to our family stroll across the park.

I began other little side projects to become more active so that I could keep up with the boys when we walked together. After two weeks with the letterbox, it was two weeks halfway down the street and back, then two weeks down the whole street and back, until it was making it around the block. Within two months, with slow and steady progress, I was able to go farther and farther joining the boys in longer walks. It was such a joy to go on these long walks together as a family.

Within nine months of the first day we started, both the boys were almost within their healthy weight ranges, just from the small changes we had made with our diet and lifestyle. Rod had come off his diabetes medication after

> ## 66
> **Yes, we live for today, but what we do today will always affect our tomorrow."**

losing 35 kilos, and Ethan had lost 16 kilos. At this stage, I had lost 32 kilos.

One wonderful tale from not so long after this is about another one of Ethan's cross-country races. My mum came to watch him, too. This time, we didn't stand at the finish line, but halfway around the circuit. As the kids started to pass us, we could see Ethan, running his hardest, and as we cheered him on, he picked up even more pace and went even harder. Our eyes filled with tears of pride and joy, our chests fit to bursting. What was also so great was how his fellow students urged him on, remembering what had happened the year before. He came third!

I'll never forget his face on finishing – it was full of smiles and pride in his own accomplishment. As the weight had come off, his confidence had grown. There was no doubt that I was the proudest mum on the oval that day!

My turn to shine

In 2013, my WW coach was Kristy Archibald. She was very excited by my weight loss and encouraged me to write about it and send my story to WW. Back then, WW had the Slimmer of the Year awards, with a category for an Inspiration Award.

I was pretty sure there were other families out there struggling and not knowing where to start, and I thought my story might help them, too, so I put pen to paper and sent it in. To my surprise, I was chosen as a finalist. My story,

alongside a few other women's, was published in *New Idea* and the public voted for the story they related to the most. A couple of weeks later, I was notified that I had won, and I was going to be flown to Sydney with Rodney to attend the WW Healthy Life awards gala.

The women at the gala were from all over Australia and New Zealand and they were all at their goal weight. I was not. I felt very insecure and shy. I remember wanting what they had achieved, reaching their goal weight and looking amazingly fit and healthy. The refrain I heard from all of them was how wonderful they felt, and I wanted to feel that, too, even more so than I already did.

That awards ceremony was the night that my *why* changed, and I discovered another new attitude. I had already achieved what I primarily set out to do: to teach Ethan a healthier way of life, and restore his confidence and belief in himself, and to help Rod come off his medication and reach his healthy weight range.

As I stood on the stage, photos of me and my boys flashed on the big screen. I held back tears of pride as I saw the pictures of our journey so far.

But right there, right then, I thought to myself, *I didn't come this far just to come this far! I am going to reach my goal weight, I am going to become fitter, I am going to see this through to the end no matter how long it takes me. I want to LIVE. I want to live to grow old with my husband, and I want to live to see my son get married, start a family of his own, and I want to be in my grandchildren's lives.*

I left the stage that night with more determination and purpose than ever before. Now it was my turn to achieve what I wanted.

It was time to focus on myself, and make myself a priority, something I had *never* done before and had always thought selfish to do. But I knew I needed to do that to keep going while also being there for my family. I felt a sense of responsibility not only to Rod and Ethan, but also to my sister – to live my life properly, a life that she was denied. To not take for granted how precious life really is.

Yes, we live for today, but what we do today will always affect our tomorrow. I've now learned the importance of making myself a priority. It was a huge step to allow myself to make that choice.

Measuring success

One of the first things I did after the gala was become more serious about exercise. Firstly, I increased the number of walks I did, working on pace and distance. We were still recovering from bankruptcy, so walking was all I could afford to do: it was free!

I learned to love this time that I took for myself. By doing it daily, it became a part of my everyday routine, a new habit if you will. I used these times to enjoy the freedom of being on my own, to get lost in my thoughts or to just feel the breeze on my face as I took in all the wonders of nature, something I'd never done before.

Next, I got a small second job to fund some new exercise. I included boxing in my routine, just once a week, and then progressed to strength training after that to help tone. As luck would have it, my WW coach Kristy had gone on to become a personal trainer, and knowing where I had started from, she helped me reach new goals. I was so in awe of what my body could do, and I pushed it a little more each time: I went for that walk, hit a boxing bag and lifted that weight.

Even so, some days it felt like it was all too much, or I became frustrated at hitting a weight-loss plateau. The longest plateau was sixteen weeks. When that happened, I stopped and reflected on why I was working so hard to achieve my goals. I also thought about beautiful Chris, and how hard her battle fighting for her life had been on a daily basis. I drew strength from her. My challenges were *nothing* compared to hers, and I knew how proud she would be of me for not giving up on myself.

I started to measure success in different ways as I didn't want to become reliant on tracking my progress just by the scales. I knew it had to be about more than just the numbers, not least because some weeks the numbers didn't play nice. And I knew some things, like going down a dress size, or being able to walk an extra 10 minutes, or not having to buy two seats on an aeroplane just for me, or wear a seatbelt extender, might take a little longer.

Even so, I keenly remember several successes that might appear small but, for me, were *huge*. These included not having my husband help me get up off the couch or floor, tying my own shoelaces again, buying my first pair of jeans since I was fourteen years old, and finally being able to go to a restaurant because I could once again fit into the seats – this was one of the biggest goals I had, and so this victory was especially sweet.

I had started to get my life back.

The person I've become

It took four years of persistence, patience and perseverance with a lot of determination, but on 19 November 2016 – I will never forget the date as it was the day before my nonna's birthday – I finally reached my goal weight. She, and my whole family, were so proud of me.

And I was proud of myself.

I had lost 70 kilos – that's an entire person, and half my body weight. The enormity of that didn't quite sink in. I used to be the size of two people, and now I am just one. I was so lucky to have had the unwavering support of my Rodney and Ethan, plus my extended family, as well as the support from WW coaches and the WW community. I HAD DONE IT!

And yet that very morning my emotions were so mixed. Everyone at the meeting cheered and clapped as tears fell freely; the joy in the room was overwhelming. I felt elated, exhausted and a sense of completion, achievement, pride, happiness … and insecurity. Yes, insecurity, and a keen sense of … *well, now what?*

I said as much to my current WW coach and now close friend, Andrea Walsh: 'What if I fail? How am I going to keep it off? How does maintaining work? All I've ever known is weight loss. This next bit is completely different.' She reassured me that I would be fine and that I'd figure it out, but I was truly scared. I felt that my safety net was gone, and that now I had reached my goal weight I had to continue alone. My fear was so real I could almost see it.

There was a six-week maintenance period before I became a lifetime member, and those six weeks really scared me. I didn't want to go backward, but I wasn't sure how to go forward. All I had known was the daily routine that I had been keeping to for the past four years. The food changed daily, yes, but my routine was the same.

Two weeks into that maintenance period, while walking down by the lake, it dawned on me that, in fact, I didn't have to do *anything* different or new. I realised that the journey I had been on didn't necessarily end at all. I realised that I still had the support of the WW community and Andrea; I still had the support of my family, and everything I had learned over four years with WW and at every single meeting would help me keep this healthy life going.

Why was this? Because it was a wellness journey, and everything I did led to permanent changes, so I was already leading and living my healthy new lifestyle. The new habits I have created and formed have become just that – new habits. I had learned so much about myself: what I am capable of and what my strengths are, as well as what my weaknesses are and how best to deal with them.

What still amazes me today is how my attitude towards weight loss in particular and life in general has changed. With any problem that arises, there is always a solution. I just look for the positive rather than a negative. I am really proud of the person I've become.

And I absolutely love walking now! I like to walk in solitude and think about what I am doing to make positive changes to my health and attitude; it keeps me focused. It's so important to feel the happiness I have inside and be content with my progress. This is my happy place, knowing and believing that I can do this. Taking time out for myself to acknowledge how far I have come, and reflect on the person I have become, has been an immense part of my journey.

Sharing my truths

I'd like to share a few truths for those of you planning your own wellness journey. Firstly, and perhaps most importantly, is not to overthink everything. There are going to be times when you will slip up, and you will have many ups and downs. Weight loss is never a straight line, so never feel guilty about a weight gain. What goes on will come off again. It's not a race. Life is for living and if you have a blowout, just make the next meal a better choice. There really is no time limit to health and success, as long as you are consistent in everything you do and learn to be patient, because we are all human.

Also, I didn't make one big decision to change my life; I made lots of little decisions along the way to help me

change my lifestyle. Indeed, my proudest moment was not reaching my goal weight, though of course I am proud of it, it was the fact that I set out to educate myself and pass that knowledge on to my family so we could make the changes to live a healthy lifestyle. That was all so we could live our best lives together, which is exactly what we're now doing.

I have now been at my goal weight for four years. Over that time I have proudly become a WW Ambassador and have continued sharing my ever-evolving story through social media with healthy recipes and updated posts to help inspire the community. I am passionate about giving back to everyone and so grateful to you all for your support. This is why I share my story, my recipes and my tips. I hope I can help you achieve your own goal by showing you how I did it and how I live the lifestyle, one day at a time.

This book is a way for me to say thank you, and I truly hope I can reignite some passion and inspiration in your daily journey and cooking for your own family. Recipes don't need to be complicated. I want to show you how easy it is to add flavour and make things look appealing. It only takes five minutes to make something look good, and then you're mostly satisfied before you even begin to eat!

Sharing my story is my way of extending help and hope to those who need it. It helps me to stay on track, too, as this is a lifelong adjustment. Consistency is the key; strive for progress, not perfection.

To all of you who have started or are planning to start your own wellness journey (or perhaps you are right in the middle of it), always remember that you are stronger than you think and you are more capable than you realise. Take each day as it comes, and try to find as much joy as you can.

I wish all of you every success on your own journey. I want you to feel the same way I do about my life now – full of hope, love and excitement for a long, bright and healthy future.

Anna xo

66

I want you to feel
the same way I do
about my life now
– full of hope, love
and excitement."

"Bringing people together through my love of food has always had a special place in my heart."

PART TWO

My Recipes

> "It's time to rise and shine."

Breakfast

Breakfast is my favourite meal of the
day. A plate of something delicious and
healthy in the morning keeps me happy
until lunchtime and sets me up for
a good day ahead.

Bacon & egg stuffed sweet potato

serves 1   prep 5 min   cook 10 min

8 **5** **2**   SmartPoints value per serve

My healthy twist on a traditional bacon-and-egg Sunday brunch. I like to use sweet potato instead of bread and load my plate with vegies – the best way to start the day.

1 small (120 g) sweet potato (kumara) (see tip)
1 teaspoon olive oil
250 g button mushrooms, sliced
½ bunch asparagus
4 cherry tomatoes on the vine
2 cups (40 g) baby spinach leaves
2 x 25 g slices short-cut bacon, fat trimmed, diced
2 eggs, lightly beaten

1 Boil, steam or microwave sweet potato until tender.

2 Heat olive oil in a non-stick frying pan over high heat. Cook mushrooms, asparagus, tomato and spinach, turning vegetables occasionally, for 2 minutes or until tender. Season with salt and pepper. Transfer to a plate and keep warm.

3 Return pan to high heat. Add bacon and cook for 2 minutes or until golden and crisp. Add eggs and cook, stirring slowly, for 1 minute or until softly scrambled.

4 Split sweet potato lengthways. Fill with bacon and egg mixture. Serve with the vegetables and season with pepper.

Anna's tip

I use a mini gold sweet potato because it is just the right size. If unavailable, use half or a third of a larger one.

Egg crepe with ricotta, mushroom & spinach

serves 1   prep 5 min   cook 5 min

 SmartPoints value per serve

I must admit I do love a sweet crepe, but this savoury crepe is really just as satisfying and delicious. Plus it's packed with protein, so it keeps me feeling full all morning.

100 g button mushrooms, sliced
**1½ cups (30 g) baby spinach
   leaves**
2 eggs
3 egg whites (see tip)
**130 g low-fat smooth
   ricotta cheese**
**flat-leaf parsley leaves,
   to garnish (optional)**

1   Lightly spray a small non-stick frying pan with oil and heat over medium–high heat. Cook mushrooms and spinach, stirring, for 2 minutes or until vegetables are softened. Season with salt and pepper. Set aside.

2   Whisk eggs and egg whites in a medium jug until frothy. Season with salt and pepper. Lightly spray a small non-stick frying pan or crepe pan with oil and heat over medium–high heat. Once hot, pour in egg mixture and cook for 15 seconds or until mixture starts to set around the edges. Using a spatula, draw the edges of the crepe into the centre, allowing the uncooked egg to run underneath. Continue doing this until the crepe is just set.

3   Carefully slide crepe onto a plate. Spoon over ricotta, then mushroom mixture, and fold over to enclose filling. Serve sprinkled with parsley, if using.

Anna's tip
You will need ⅓ cup (80 ml)
egg whites.

Caramelised onion & mushrooms on sourdough

serves 2   prep 5 min   cook 20 min

 SmartPoints value per serve

Just thinking about the smell of mushrooms and onion caramelising in the kitchen makes my mouth water! I recommend trying this recipe when you have a bit of extra time on the weekend, so that you can really enjoy making (and eating!) it.

1 teaspoon garlic-infused olive oil
1 large white onion,
  finely chopped
125 g Swiss brown mushrooms,
  sliced
125 g button mushrooms, sliced
1 tablespoon chopped thyme
1 tablespoon chopped flat-leaf
  parsley, plus extra to serve
8 cherry tomatoes on the vine
2 eggs
2 x 35 g slices wholemeal
  sourdough bread, toasted

1   Preheat oven to 180°C. Heat oil in a medium non-stick frying pan over medium–low heat. Cook onion, stirring for 10 minutes or until starting to brown. Add mushrooms and thyme and cook, stirring occasionally, for 10 minutes or until caramelised and there is no liquid in the pan. Season with salt and pepper and stir through the parsley.

2   Meanwhile, place tomatoes on a small baking tray and bake for 10 minutes or until tender.

3   Bring a large deep frying pan of water to the boil, reduce heat to low. Carefully break 1 egg into a cup, then slide into water. Repeat with remaining egg. Poach eggs gently for 1–2 minutes or until egg whites are set and yolks are still soft. Cook a minute or two longer if you like your yolk firm.

4   Top each slice of toast with mushrooms, a poached egg and a sprinkle of extra parsley.

Anna's tip

If you eat dairy, grate over 1 teaspoon parmesan at no extra SmartPoints.

Natural cinnamon muesli

serves 18   makes 4½ cups   prep 10 min

 3 3 2   **SmartPoints value per serve**

Given that I love muesli as much as I love oats, I decided to make my own. The great thing is that I know exactly what's in it, plus I can tweak the flavours to my liking and it's so much cheaper than the store-bought version.

2 cups (180 g) traditional (whole) rolled oats
½ cup (40 g) toasted flaked almonds (see tips)
⅔ cup (150 g) chopped pitted medjool dates
½ cup (80 g) reduced-sugar dried cranberries
½ cup (75 g) pepitas (pumpkin seeds), toasted (see tips)
¼ cup (35 g) sunflower seeds
¼ cup (12 g) coconut flakes
2 tablespoons hemp seeds (see tips)
1 teaspoon ground cinnamon
¼ teaspoon salt

1 Combine all ingredients in a large bowl.

2 The muesli can be stored in an airtight container for up to 2 months.

Anna's tips

* Serve with your favourite milk or 99% fat-free yoghurt. Check your WW app for SmartPoints.
* Toasting the almonds and pepitas gives this muesli mix a bit more flavour and crunch. Simply dry-fry them in a non-stick frying pan over very low heat, stirring to make sure they don't burn, until they turn light golden.
* You can use flaxseeds instead of hemp seeds.

Pumpkin spiced pancakes

serves 2   prep 10 min   cook 10 min

 SmartPoints value per serve

I love pancakes for breakfast but they can be a bit too sweet first thing, so here's my recipe for savoury spiced pancakes. Pumpkin spice is one of my favourite spice mixes. I make my own, as it's very easy and I use it in a variety of dishes. These pancakes are great simply served with bacon, but I also enjoy eating them with a side of wilted spinach and a fried egg. It's an amazing combination – give it a try!

¼ cup (35 g) self-raising flour
½ teaspoon baking powder
1 teaspoon pumpkin pie spice
   or ground cinnamon (see tips)
½ cup (85 g) cooked and mashed
   pumpkin (see tips)
2 eggs, lightly beaten
4 x 25 g slices short-cut bacon,
   fat trimmed
2 teaspoons sugar-free
   maple syrup

1 Place flour, baking powder, pumpkin spice, mashed pumpkin and eggs in a bowl. Whisk until smooth.

2 Lightly spray a large non-stick frying pan with olive oil and heat over medium heat. Spoon 2 tablespoon amounts of batter into pan to make 3 pancakes. Cook for 2 minutes or until bubbles appear on surface of pancake. Flip and cook for 1 minute or until golden and cooked through. Repeat to make 6 pancakes.

3 Meanwhile, heat a small non-stick frying pan over high heat. Cook bacon for 2 minutes each side or until golden and crisp. Divide pancakes and bacon among plates and serve with a drizzle of maple syrup.

Anna's tips

* I make my own pumpkin spice mix by combining 2 tablespoons ground cinnamon, 2 teaspoons ground ginger, 1 teaspoon each ground cloves and mixed spice, ½ teaspoon each ground nutmeg and cardamom and ¼ teaspoon salt. This makes ½ cup (about 20 g). Store in an airtight container for 6–12 months.
* I love to meal prep pumpkin at the beginning of the week so I always have it ready in the fridge to make delicious recipes like this one.

GLUTEN-FREE CARROT CAKE

CHOCOLATE WEET-BIX

PEAR & RASPBERRY OAT BRAN

90-second mug muffins

If you haven't jumped on the mug-muffin bandwagon, I highly recommend you do!
They are extremely quick to make, super filling and absolutely delicious.

Turn the page for recipes >

BANANA

APPLE & CINNAMON

Chocolate Weet-Bix mug muffin

serves 1 prep 5 min cook 1½ min

6 3 3 SmartPoints value per serve

This recipe came about when I had a big box of Weet-Bix in the pantry and I thought I'd have a go creating something new. I make this for my son as he loves chocolate for breakfast – he has absolutely no idea how healthy it is!

1 Weet-Bix, crushed
1 egg
1 tablespoon cocoa powder,
    plus extra to serve
1 large ripe banana, mashed
100 g 99% fat-free plain yoghurt
1 tablespoon strawberries
1 tablespoon raspberries
mint leaves, to serve (optional)

1 Combine Weet-Bix, egg, cocoa and banana in a small bowl.

2 Rinse a microwave-safe mug out with boiling water to prevent muffin from sticking. Spoon mixture into prepared mug and microwave on High (100%) for 90 seconds or until muffin starts to come away from the sides of the mug and is just firm to touch.

3 Serve muffin sprinkled with extra cocoa and with yoghurt, berries and mint leaves, if you like.

Gluten-free carrot cake mug muffin

serves 1 prep 5 min cook 1½ min

6 3 0 SmartPoints value per serve

Who doesn't love carrot cake? As I often find myself craving a huge slice of it, I decided to make an individual serve in a mug-muffin form. Using quinoa flakes gives it a more cake-like texture – and, as a bonus, it's also gluten free.

30 g quinoa flakes
1 egg
1 teaspoon mixed spice
1 large ripe banana, mashed
2 tablespoons grated carrot
1–2 pitted medjool dates, chopped
100 g 99% fat-free plain yoghurt
berries, to serve
ground cinnamon, to sprinkle

1 Combine quinoa, egg, spice, banana, carrot and date in a small bowl.

2 Rinse a microwave-safe mug out with boiling water to prevent muffin from sticking. Spoon mixture into prepared mug and microwave on High (100%) for 90 seconds or until muffin starts to come away from the sides of the mug and is just firm to touch.

3 Serve muffin with yoghurt and fresh berries, and sprinkled with cinnamon.

Pear & raspberry oat bran mug muffin

serves 1 prep 5 min cook 1½ min

7 3 3 SmartPoints value per serve

I like to play with a variety of textures with my mug muffins, and oat bran is a winner here. With juicy pears and sweet raspberries, this muffin can easily be a dessert option, too.

30 g oat bran
1 egg
150 g mashed pear
    (store-bought or cooked)
½ teaspoon ground cinnamon
⅓ cup (50 g) raspberries, halved,
    plus 2 tablespoons to serve
100 g unsweetened plain soy
    yoghurt, to serve

1 Combine oat bran, egg, pear and cinnamon in a small bowl. Gently fold in halved raspberries.

2 Rinse a microwave-safe mug out with boiling water to prevent muffin from sticking. Spoon mixture into prepared mug and microwave on High (100%) for 90 seconds or until muffin starts to come away from the sides of the mug and is just firm to touch.

3 Serve muffin topped with yoghurt and remaining berries.

Banana mug muffin

serves 1 prep 5 min cook 1½ min

6 3 0 SmartPoints value per serve

Here's a really good basic recipe. Feel free to add your own flavour variations and don't forget to share your delicious creations with me!

⅓ cup (30 g) quick oats
1 ripe banana, mashed
1 egg
pinch ground cinnamon, plus extra to serve
2 pitted medjool dates, chopped
¼ cup (60 g) 99% fat-free plain yoghurt
blueberries, to serve

1 Combine oats, banana, egg, cinnamon and date in a small bowl.

2 Rinse a microwave-safe mug out with boiling water to prevent muffin from sticking. Spoon mixture into prepared mug and microwave on High (100%) for 90 seconds or until muffin starts to come away from the sides of the mug and is just firm to touch.

3 Serve muffin topped with yoghurt, blueberries and extra cinnamon.

Apple & cinnamon mug muffin

serves 1 prep 5 min cook 1½ min

6 3 0 SmartPoints value per serve

I love experimenting with flavour combinations, and apple and cinnamon is one of my favourite pairings. This mug muffin reminds me of apple pie – yum.

⅓ cup (30 g) quick oats
1 egg
½ teaspoon ground cinnamon, plus extra to serve
150 g mashed apple (store-bought or cooked)
¼ cup (60 g) 99% fat-free plain yoghurt
sliced apple, to serve

1 Combine oats, egg, cinnamon and apple in a small bowl.

2 Rinse a microwave-safe mug out with boiling water to prevent muffin from sticking. Spoon mixture into prepared mug and microwave on High (100%) for 90 seconds or until muffin starts to come away from the sides of the mug and is just firm to touch.

3 Serve muffin topped with yoghurt, sliced apple and extra cinnamon.

The best hearty breakfast

serves 1   prep 5 min   cook 10 min

 SmartPoints value per serve

This is one of my absolute favourite breakfasts! Best of all, it's ready in 15 minutes so I don't even have to wait for the weekend to enjoy it.

1 small (120 g) sweet potato (kumara)
3 x 25 g slices short-cut bacon, fat trimmed
1 teaspoon garlic-infused olive oil
125 g button mushrooms, sliced
6 cherry tomatoes, halved
50 g baby spinach leaves
2 eggs

1 Boil, steam or microwave sweet potato until tender. Drain.

2 Meanwhile, heat a non-stick frying pan over medium–high heat. Cook bacon for 2 minutes each side or until golden and crisp. Transfer to a plate. Add oil to pan and reheat over medium heat. Cook mushroom and tomatoes, turning occasionally, for 2 minutes or until tender. Season with salt and pepper. Push to one side and add spinach, cook, stirring, for 1–2 minutes or until just wilted.

3 Meanwhile, whisk eggs and 2 tablespoons water in a bowl until well combined. Lightly spray a small non-stick frying pan with oil and heat over medium heat. Add egg mixture and cook, stirring slowly, for 1 minute or until softly scrambled.

4 Serve eggs with bacon, spinach and sweet potato, along with button mushrooms and cherry tomatoes. Season with pepper.

Homemade potato waffle

sserves 1   prep 10 min   cook 5 min

 SmartPoints value per serve

Just like a big ol' hash brown in waffle form … yes, please. Super filling and super easy, savoury waffles have become a favourite all-in-one-dish in our house. At the photoshoot, I served them a couple of extras – a dollop of light sour cream and a sprinkle of chives (see tips) – and they were amazing!

200 g reduced-carb potato (see tips)
1 egg, lighty beaten
1 egg white, lightly beaten
20 g grated mozzarella cheese
20 g diced honey leg ham
½ cup (10 g) baby spinach leaves
¼ red onion, diced
½ teaspoon mixed herbs

1 Grate potato and place in a clean kitchen cloth. Squeeze out excess moisture. Combine potato, egg, egg white, mozzarella, ham, spinach, onion and herbs in a medium bowl. Season with salt and pepper.

2 Preheat waffle maker on high heat. Once hot, lightly spray with oil and add batter to make one waffle. Cook for 5 minutes or until golden and cooked through. Serve with sour cream and chives, if you like (see tips).

Anna's tips

* Find low-carb potatoes in the fresh produce section of the supermarket in packets.
* You can check the SmartPoints of the light sour cream using your WW app.

Ricotta, broccoli & caramelised onion breakfast muffins

makes 12   prep 10 min   cook 40 min

 SmartPoints value per serve

This is a perfect breakfast on the go. I made these one morning when I had some leftover onion from dinner the night before and some ricotta I needed to use up. The flavour combination just worked, and they've been a staple ever since.

1 teaspoon garlic-infused olive oil

3 large onions, thinly sliced

1 cup (240 g) low-fat smooth ricotta cheese

8 eggs

1 tablespoon thyme leaves

1 tablespoon chopped flat-leaf parsley

2 cups (190 g) finely chopped broccoli

12 cherry tomatoes

1 Preheat oven to 180°C. Heat oil in a large non-stick frying pan over low heat. Cook onion, stirring occasionally, for 15 minutes or until caramelised. Set aside to cool.

2 Whisk ricotta and eggs in large bowl until smooth. Add thyme, parsley, broccoli, and onions and stir until well combined. Spoon mixture into 12 (½ cup/125 ml capacity) silicone muffin moulds. Place moulds on a baking tray and bake for 20 minutes. Add a cherry tomato to the top of each muffin. Bake for a further 15 minutes or until golden and set.

Vegetarian breakfast bowl

serves 1 prep 10 min cook 10 min

 SmartPoints value per serve

Have you ever tried pan-frying chickpeas? It gives them a lovely crispy texture, and adding just a little spice delivers a huge flavour boost. This vegie meal is so satisfying and it will keep your energy levels steady all morning.

½ small (60 g) sweet potato
  (kumara)
2 eggs
1 teaspoon olive oil
125 g button mushrooms, sliced
6 cherry tomatoes
½ cup (90 g) drained and rinsed
  canned chickpeas
½ teaspoon paprika
2 cups (40 g) baby spinach leaves

1 Boil, steam or microwave potato until tender. Drain.

2 Meanwhile, whisk eggs and 2 tablespoons water in a small bowl until well combined (see tip). Heat oil in a medium non-stick frying pan over high heat. Cook mushrooms and tomatoes, stirring, for 3–4 minutes or until golden. Transfer to a serving bowl.

3 Return pan to high heat. Add chickpeas and paprika and cook, stirring, for 1–2 minutes or until warmed through. Push chickpeas to one side of pan, add spinach and cook until just wilted. Transfer chickpeas and spinach to bowl with mushrooms. Add egg mixture to pan and cook, stirring slowly, for 1 minute or until softly scrambled.

4 Add eggs and sweet potato to bowl with mushrooms and tomatoes. Season with salt and pepper to serve.

Anna's tip
Whisking a little water with your eggs makes them really fluffy and light.

Cinnamon French toast with caramelised banana

serves 2   prep 5 min   cook 5 min

 SmartPoints value per serve

To my mind, anything with cinnamon is going to taste good, but with classic French toast it's truly incredible. Caramelised bananas are lovely and sweet, but not over-indulgent – if you have never tried them, you should!

2 eggs
1 teaspoon ground cinnamon,
   plus extra to serve
1 tablespoon sugar-free
   maple syrup
1 teaspoon reduced-fat oil spread
4 x 35 g slices wholemeal
   sourdough bread
1 banana, halved lengthways
berries, to serve

1 Whisk the eggs, cinnamon and maple syrup in a medium bowl until combined.

2 Heat spread in a large non-stick frying pan over medium–high heat. Working one at a time, dip bread into egg mixture until well soaked. Cook for 1–2 minutes each side or until golden. Transfer toast to serving plates.

3 Add banana to pan and cook for 1 minute each side or until caramelised. Serve French toast with the caramelised banana and berries and an extra sprinkle of cinnamon.

Overnight oats

Breakfast made the night before is a winner in three ways: it helps you stay on track, saves on the washing up and gives you an extra 10 minutes in bed.

Turn the page for recipes >

LAMINGTON

MANGO & COCONUT

STRAWBERRIES & CREAM

50% **Weight Lost** | 100% **Healthier**

BLUEBERRY
& LEMON
CHEESECAKE

APPLE PIE
WITH SALTED
DATE CARAMEL

Mango & coconut overnight oats

serves 2   prep 5 min

 8 **6** **3**   SmartPoints value per serve

When mango is in season, try pairing it with oats for a tropical delight.

**1 cup (240 g) 99% fat-free plain
  yoghurt**
**⅔ cup (60 g) quick-cook or
  traditional (whole) rolled oats**
¼ cup (60 ml) light coconut cream
**2 tablespoons sugar-free maple
  syrup**
1 mango, chopped
2 small bananas, thinly sliced
berries and mint leaves, to serve

1 Combine yoghurt, oats, coconut cream and maple syrup in a bowl.

2 Layer the mango, oat mixture and banana in two 1½ cup (375 ml) capacity jars, finishing with a layer of oats. Cover and refrigerate overnight (see tips). Top with berries and mint.

Anna's tips

* If your oat mixture is too thick, try adding 30–50 ml unsweetened vanilla almond milk (or a nut-free alternative).

* If you're using quick oats, you only need to refrigerate for 1–2 hours.

* To serve the oats warm, heat in a microwave on High (100%) for 1 minute and add toppings before serving.

Lamington overnight oats

serves 2   prep 10 min

 7 **6** **2**   SmartPoints value per serve

Now you can enjoy lamington cake for breakfast any day of the week.

Bottom layer
1 cup (140 g) raspberries, crushed
2 teaspoons chia seeds

Middle layer
**⅔ cup (60 g) traditional (whole)
  rolled oats**
**⅔ cup (160 g) 99% fat-free plain
  yoghurt**
**½ cup (125 ml) unsweetened coconut
  almond milk**
1 teaspoon vanilla extract

Top layer
**2 tablespoons sugar-free maple
  syrup**
**2 teaspoons raw cacao or cocoa
  powder**
raspberries, to serve
**2 teaspoons shredded coconut,
  to serve**

1 Combine crushed raspberries and chia seeds in the base of two 1½ cup (375 ml) capacity glass jars to make bottom layer.

2 Combine oats, yoghurt, milk and vanilla in a bowl. Spoon into jars to make middle layer.

3 Combine maple syrup and cocoa in a bowl. Layer cocoa mixture on top of oat mixture. Cover and refrigerate overnight (see tips) Top with raspberries and coconut.

Strawberries & cream overnight oats

serves 2   prep 10 mins

 8 **7** **2**   SmartPoints value per serve

Healthy strawberries and cream! I love experimenting with different flavours and this combo has to be one of my top ones.

**250 g strawberries, plus extra
  to serve**
**1 cup (90 g) quick-cook or traditional
  (whole) rolled oats**
**¾ cup (180 ml) unsweetened vanilla
  almond milk**
**½ cup (120 g) 99% fat-free plain
  yoghurt**
**pinch ground cinnamon,
  plus extra to serve**
100 g low-fat smooth ricotta cheese
1 tablespoon sugar-free maple syrup

1 Process half the strawberries in a food processor to a smooth puree. Alternatively, place in a bowl and crush with a fork.

2 Combine oats, milk, yoghurt, cinnamon and strawberry puree in a bowl. Divide oat mixture between two 1½ cup (375 ml) capacity jars.

3 Slice remaining strawberries and layer on top of oat mixture. Combine ricotta and maple syrup in a bowl until smooth. Spoon ricotta mixture over strawberries. Cover and refrigerate overnight (see tips). Serve topped with extra strawberries plus a sprinkle of cinnamon.

Blueberry & lemon cheesecake overnight oats

serves 2   prep 15 min

8 **7** **2**   SmartPoints value per serve

Cheesecake for breakfast? Oh yes.

1 cup (260 g) frozen blueberries
1 cup (90 g) quick-cook or traditional (whole) rolled oats
½ cup (125 ml) unsweetened vanilla almond milk
½ cup (120 g) 99% fat-free plain yoghurt
1 tablespoon sugar-free maple syrup
2 teaspoons finely grated lemon zest
2 tablespoons lemon juice

Cheesecake topping
65 g low-fat smooth ricotta cheese
30 g spreadable light cream cheese
½ teaspoon sugar-free maple syrup
1 teaspoon finely grated lemon zest
blueberries and mint leaves, to serve

1 Place blueberries in a microwave-safe dish. Cover and microwave on High (100%) for 2–3 minutes or until softened. Crush with a fork. Set aside to cool.

2 Combine oats, milk, yoghurt, maple syrup, zest, juice and crushed blueberries in a bowl. Divide oat mixture between two 1½ cup (375 ml) capacity jars.

3 Combine ricotta, cream cheese, maple syrup and zest in a bowl. Top oat mixture with cheesecake mixture. Cover and refrigerate overnight (see tips). Serve topped with blueberries and mint.

Apple pie with salted date caramel overnight oats

serves 2   prep 10 min   cook 5 min

7 **6** **1**   SmartPoints value per serve

The salted date caramel in this recipe is easy to make and can be used in so many ways, from sweetening cakes, mixing with yoghurt or dolloping on ice cream. It's hard to resist eating it straight out of the jar by itself.

2 apples, plus extra sliced apple, to serve
pinch ground cinnamon
1 cup (90 g) quick-cook or traditional (whole) rolled oats
¾ cup (180 ml) unsweetened almond milk
½ cup (120 g) 99% fat-free plain yoghurt
2 teaspoons salted date caramel

Salted date caramel
makes 1 cup (250 g)

0 **0** **0**   SmartPoints value per teaspoon

180 g pitted medjool dates
2 teaspoons sea salt flakes

1 Dice 1 apple. Combine diced apple, cinnamon and 1 tablespoon water in a microwave-safe dish. Microwave on High (100%) for 2–3 minutes or until softened. Spoon cooked apple into the base of two 1½ cup (375 ml) capacity serving jars.

2 Grate 1 apple. Combine grated apple, oats, almond milk and yoghurt in a bowl and divide among jars. Cover and refrigerate overnight (see tips).

3 To make the salted date caramel, place dates, sea salt and ½ cup (125 ml) boiling water in a food processor and leave for 10 minutes, then process until smooth and creamy. Spoon into a 1 cup (250 ml) capacity sterilised jar. Store in the fridge for up to 3 months.

4 Serve oats topped with 2 teaspoons salted caramel and extra sliced apple.

Snacking
without the
stress."

Snacks

I tend to need a little something
extra throughout the day, especially
if I'm exercising. Prepping is key here.
Having healthy, SmartPoints-friendly
options ready to go in the fridge
or freezer takes all the stress out
of snacking.

Leek, mushroom & feta frittata muffins

makes 14   prep 10 min   cook 25 min

 SmartPoints value per serve

One morning, I had a heap of eggs to use up along with some odds and ends in the fridge. The result? These frittata-style muffins, which I enjoyed as snacks throughout the week. Even better, they take no time at all to whip up. I've kept them vegetarian but you could add a bit of bacon if you feel like it.

300 g button mushrooms, sliced

3 leeks, thinly sliced

2–3 garlic cloves, crushed

½ cup (75 g) self-raising flour

100 g semi-dried tomatoes (oil-free), finely chopped

8 eggs

70 g reduced-fat Greek feta cheese

½ cup flat-leaf parsley leaves, coarsely chopped

1   Heat a large non-stick frying pan over medium heat. Cook mushrooms, leek and garlic, stirring, for 5–6 minutes or until light golden. Season with salt and pepper. Transfer to a large bowl and set aside to cool.

2   Preheat oven to 180°C. Add flour, tomato and eggs to mushroom mixture and stir to combine. Season with salt and pepper.

3   Spoon mixture among 14 (½ cup/125 ml capacity) silicone muffin moulds (or use muffin tins lined with paper cases). Top each with some crumbled feta. Bake for 20 minutes or until golden and just set.

4   Cool muffins in their moulds for 5 minutes before transferring to a wire rack to cool. Sprinkle with chopped parsley, to serve.

Bliss balls

Like all my recipes, these nutritious snacks are super quick and easy – you'll need a whole 15 minutes to make them!

Turn the page for recipes >

APPLE PIE

MOCHA MAPLE

CHOCOLATE
BROWNIE

CHERRY
RIPE

HOT CROSS BUN

CHOCOLATE
WEET-BIX

59

Apple pie bliss balls

makes 15   prep 15 min

 2 **2** **1**   SmartPoints value per ball

Who doesn't love the flavours of apple pie? These were a total experiment with an absolutely fabulous result! They disappeared very quickly: a big tick of approval from my boys.

100 g traditional (whole) rolled oats
12 medjool dates, pitted
1 tablespoon sugar-free maple syrup
2 tablespoons apple puree (see tip)
30 g desiccated coconut
½ teaspoon vanilla essence
½ teaspoon ground nutmeg
1 teaspoon ground cinnamon

1   Process oats, dates, maple syrup, apple puree, coconut, vanilla, nutmeg, cinnamon and a pinch of salt in a food processor until well combined.

2   Using damp hands, roll the mixture into 15 balls. Cover and place in fridge for 1 hour or until firm.

Anna's tip

I make my own apple puree by cooking apple and mashing it. You can also buy no-added-sugar apple puree at the supermarket.

Mocha maple bliss balls

makes 20   prep 15 min

 1 **1** **0**   SmartPoints value per ball

Seriously, I think these are the best bliss balls I've ever created. The taste is just INCREDIBLE. If you love mocha, please give these a go – they are so moreish. If you make them and love them, spread the word!

50 g dry-roasted almonds
12 medjool dates, pitted
1 cup (90 g) traditional (whole) rolled oats
80 g sugar-free drinking chocolate
1 tablespoon sugar-free maple syrup
2 tablespoons cold espresso (see tip)

1   Process almonds in a food processor until finely chopped. Add dates and pulse until dates are coarsely chopped. Add oats, 60 g drinking chocolate, maple syrup and coffee, and process until well combined.

2   Place remaining drinking chocolate on a plate. Using damp hands, roll the mixture into 20 balls. Roll in drinking chocolate to coat. Cover and place in fridge for 1 hour or until firm.

Anna's tip

If you don't have a coffee machine, no problem – just use instant coffee powder dissolved in 2 tablespoons hot water.

Hot cross bun bliss balls

makes 20   prep 15 min

 1 **1** **1**   SmartPoints value per ball

I couldn't be happier with the flavour of these! I make a triple batch and freeze them the week before Easter. Yep, they are that good.

12 medjool dates, pitted
100 g dry-roasted almonds
2 teaspoons finely grated orange zest
1 tablespoon orange juice
2 teaspoons pure maple syrup
½ teaspoon sea salt
½ teaspoon mixed spice
1 teaspoon ground cinnamon
½ teaspoon ground ginger
½ teaspoon ground nutmeg
2 tablespoons currants

1   Process dates, almonds, zest, juice, maple syrup, salt, mixed spice, cinnamon, ginger and nutmeg in a food processor until well combined. Add currants and process until just combined.

2   Using damp hands, roll the mixture into 20 balls. Cover and place in fridge for 1 hour or until firm.

Chocolate brownie bliss balls

makes 20 prep 15 min

 SmartPoints value per ball

These are sweet, rich and fudgy – just like chocolate brownies but in bliss ball form.

½ cup (50 g) walnuts
100 g traditional (whole) rolled oats
2 tablespoons sugar-free maple syrup
¼ cup (30 g) sugar-free drinking chocolate
2 teaspoons vanilla essence
12 medjool dates, pitted

1 Process walnuts, oats, maple syrup, drinking chocolate, vanilla, dates and a pinch of salt in a food processor until well combined.

2 Using damp hands, roll the mixture into 20 balls. Cover and place in fridge for 1 hour or until firm.

Cherry ripe bliss balls

makes 20 prep 15 min

 SmartPoints value per ball

When cherries are in season, I just can't resist them! My husband, who only likes them covered in chocolate, asked me if I could make a Cherry Ripe for him. Ummm, no – but I can make bliss balls! How's that for a compromise?

100 g traditional (whole) rolled oats
2 tablespoons cocoa powder
12 medjool dates, pitted
2 teaspoons sugar-free maple syrup
½ cup (75 g) cherries, pitted
¼ cup (20 g) desiccated coconut

1 Process oats, cocoa powder, dates, maple syrup, cherries, 1 tablespoon coconut and a pinch of salt in a food processor until well combined.

2 Place remaining coconut on a plate. Using damp hands, roll the mixture into 20 balls. Roll in coconut to coat. Cover and place in fridge for 1 hour or until firm.

Chocolate Weet-Bix bliss balls

makes 20 prep 15 min

 SmartPoints value per ball

Remember Weet-Bix slice? Growing up, we kids absolutely loved it. My boys asked me to make a healthier version of this classic treat. With just five ingredients, this is a really quick and easy snack that kids and adults alike can enjoy.

12 medjool dates, pitted
5 Weet-Bix
2 teaspoons golden syrup
½ cup (40 g) desiccated coconut
20 g cocoa powder

1 Process dates in a food processor until roughly chopped. Add Weet-Bix, golden syrup, ¼ cup (20 g) coconut and cocoa, and process until well combined.

2 Place remaining coconut on a plate. Using damp hands, roll the mixture into 20 balls. Roll in coconut to coat. Cover and place in fridge for 1 hour or until firm.

Anna's tip
You can use gluten-free Weet-Bix in this recipe.

Hawaiian pizza bites

prep 5 min   cook 5 min   serves 2

 SmartPoints value per serve

If you love pineapple pizza, then you'll love this lighter version – it's super quick and easy!

1 tablespoon garlic, onion & herb pizza sauce
1 x 65 g wholemeal English muffin, split
50 g shaved ham
2 tablespoons crushed pineapple
2 tablespoons grated reduced-fat cheddar cheese
1 tablespoon chopped flat-leaf parsley

1   Preheat grill on high. Spread pizza sauce over cut side of muffin halves. Top with ham, pineapple and cheddar.

2   Grill for 1–2 minutes or until cheese is melted and bubbling. Sprinkle with parsley and serve immediately.

My favourite dips

I much prefer to make my own dips rather than buying them from the shop.
Not only is this the healthier option, it's cheaper too.

Turn the page for recipes >

**TUNA SALAD
DIP**

**CREAMY
HUMMUS**

**FRENCH
ONION DIP**

**HOMEMADE
TZATZIKI**

Tuna salad dip

serves 2   prep 10 min

4 **2** **2**   SmartPoints value per serve

This substantial dip is incredibly easy and magnificently delicious. I love to serve it on a platter with sliced cucumber, cherry tomatoes, carrot sticks, boiled eggs and cubed cheese, along with grapes and blueberries.

2 x 95 g cans tuna in spring water, drained and flaked
2 tablespoons 99% fat-free plain yoghurt
1 tablespoon low-fat mayonnaise
¼ red onion, finely chopped
5–6 cherry tomatoes, diced
¼ cup flat-leaf parsley or basil leaves, finely sliced

1 Combine all ingredients in a small bowl. Season with salt and pepper.

Creamy hummus

serves 8   prep 10 min

1 **0** **0**   SmartPoints value per serve

Hummus is one of my all-time favourites. I make enough for 8 serves and store the rest in the fridge. It's a lovely addition to any sandwich and can be used as a salad dressing.

400 g can chickpeas, drained and rinsed
1 tablespoon 99% fat-free plain yoghurt
2 teaspoons finely grated lemon zest
1 tablespoon lemon juice
1–2 garlic cloves, grated

1 Process chickpeas, yoghurt, zest, juice, 1 tablespoon water and garlic in a small food processor until well combined and creamy (process longer if you like it smooth). Season with salt and pepper.

Anna's tip
One serve is equal to 2 tablespoons.

50% **Weight Lost** | 100% **Healthier**

French onion dip

serves 2   prep 5 min

2 1 1   SmartPoints value per serve

Dip doesn't get any easier than this. Just TWO ingredients mixed together makes this magic happen. Scale up for parties – it's always a crowd-pleaser.

1 tablespoon French onion soup mix
1 cup (240 g) 99% fat-free plain yoghurt

1 Process soup mix in a small food processor or blender until it is a fine powder. Combine yoghurt and soup mix in a small bowl and serve.

Homemade tzatziki

serves 4   prep 15 min

1 0 0   SmartPoints value per serve

This classic Greek dip is so easy to whip up, especially as the ingredients are usually in my fridge ready to go, making it perfect for a last-minute platter.

1 Lebanese cucumber, peeled, halved
  lengthways, deseeded
1 cup (240 g) 99% fat-free plain yoghurt
1 garlic clove, grated
1 teaspoon finely grated lemon zest
1 tablespoon lemon juice
1 tablespoon chopped mint

1 Coarsely grate and drain cucumber (see tip). Combine yoghurt, garlic, zest, juice, mint and cucumber in a medium bowl. Season with salt and pepper.

Anna's tip
I wrap the grated cucumber in a clean kitchen cloth and squeeze gently to remove the liquid.

Vegan broccoli, cauliflower & carrot bites

makes 20   serves 4   prep 15 min   cook 15 min

3 **3** **3**   SmartPoints value per serve

A lovely friend of mine who is vegan asked me if I could make something to add to her snack boxes. I came up with these little vegetable bites, and everyone enjoyed them so much that I ended up making a second – and then a third – batch.

300 g cauliflower and broccoli rice (see tip)
1 carrot, grated
¼ cup chopped flat-leaf parsley
30 g nutritional yeast
2 tablespoons reduced-fat hummus
¼ cup (50 g) rice flour

1 Preheat oven to 180°C. Line a baking tray with baking paper.

2 Place cauliflower and broccoli rice in a microwave-safe dish with the carrot. Cover and microwave on High (100%) for 2 minutes or until just tender. Set aside to cool.

3 Add parsley, nutritional yeast, hummus and rice flour to the vegetables and stir until well combined. Shape tablespoons of mixture into bite-sized nuggets. Place bites on prepared tray and lightly spray with oil. Bake for 15 minutes or until golden.

Anna's tip
Cauliflower and broccoli rice is available from large supermarkets.

50% **Weight Lost** | 100% **Healthier**

Pea, corn & bacon loaves

makes 6   prep 10 min   cook 30 min

4 **0** **0**   **SmartPoints value per loaf**

I made this using leftover bits and pieces in the fridge and it came together brilliantly. These are wonderful served for breakfast or lunch, as well as a snack, and are equally delicious hot or cold.

6 eggs, lightly beaten
2 corn cobs, kernels removed
1 cup (120 g) frozen peas
100 g short-cut bacon,
   fat trimmed, diced
½ red onion, finely chopped
⅓ cup finely sliced basil

1 Preheat oven to 180°C. Line bases of a 6-hole (200 ml capacity) mini loaf tin with baking paper.

2 Combine eggs, corn, peas, bacon, onion and basil in a large bowl. Season with salt and pepper. Divide mixture among prepared loaf holes. Bake for 20–30 minutes or until golden and set. Cool in tin for 5 minutes before transferring to a wire rack to cool.

Mountain bread spring rolls

makes 32   prep 15 min   cook 30 min

 SmartPoints value per spring roll

I can't pretend these are proper spring rolls, but these low-fat, low-SmartPoints snacks are so delicious and crunchy, they never last long and they suit my way of eating just perfectly.

500 g chicken breast mince
3 garlic cloves, grated
1 tablespoon grated ginger
175 g bean sprouts
200 g packet coleslaw
  (no dressing)
3 teaspoons kecap manis
  (Indonesian sweet soy sauce)
1 tablespoon chilli garlic sauce
8 x 25 g rye mountain bread
  wraps (see tips)
lime wedges, to serve
sliced green shallots, to serve

1   Heat a large non-stick frying pan over medium–high heat. Add mince, garlic and ginger, and cook, stirring to break up any lumps, for 5 minutes or until browned. Add bean sprouts, coleslaw, kecap manis and chilli garlic sauce, and cook, stirring, for 2 minutes or until the veg are tender. Set aside to cool.

2   Preheat oven to 200°C. Line a baking tray with baking paper. Cut wraps into quarters. Working one at a time, place 2 tablespoons of filling diagonally across one corner. Fold this corner over the filling, then fold the two sides into the centre. Roll to enclose filling. Repeat with remaining wraps and filling.

3   Place spring rolls, seam-side down, on prepared tray and lightly spray with oil. Bake for 10–15 minutes or until golden and crisp. Cut each roll into 4 pieces and serve with lime wedges, sliced shallots and light sweet chilli sauce, if you like (see tips).

Anna's tips

* You can replace mountain bread with filo pastry; use 16 sheets for the same SmartPoints.
* You can freeze these, uncooked, for up to 1 month.
* Serve with 3 tablespoons light sweet chilli sauce for dipping at no extra SmartPoints.

Anna's snack boxes

Feel free to mix and match these do-ahead ideas and create your own boxes for home, work, on the road or even trips to the movies.

Turn the page for recipes >

Greek snack box
See page 74

GREEK MINI MEATBALLS
page 74

HOMEMADE CHICKEN NUGGETS
page 75

CREAMY HUMMUS
page 66

School snack box
See page 75

Work snack box
See page 76

FRENCH
ONION DIP
page 67

MOCHA MAPLE
BLISS BALLS
page 60

CHICKEN,
SPINACH & FETA
PATTIES
page 76

**Vegetarian
snack box**
See page 77

HOMEMADE
TZATZIKI
page 67

BEETROOT
FALAFEL
page 77

GREEK SNACK BOX

5 Greek mini meatballs

1 **0** **0** SmartPoints value per serve

+

9 rice crackers

2 **2** **2** SmartPoints value per serve

+

sticks of carrot, capsicum and cucumber

+

strawberries and blueberries

Greek mini meatballs

serves 5 prep 15 min cook 10 min

1 **0** **0** SmartPoints value per serve

The flavours of these meatballs take me to Greece, with the strong hints of oregano and garlic. These are perfect for a share platter as well as in a snack box.

500 g chicken breast mince
1 red onion, finely chopped
¼ cup chopped flat-leaf parsley
1 tablespoon chopped mint
1 teaspoon dried oregano
2 garlic cloves, grated
2 teaspoons finely grated lemon zest

1 Preheat oven to 180°C. Line a baking tray with baking paper.

2 Combine mince, onion, parsley, mint, oregano, garlic and zest in a medium bowl. Season with salt and pepper. Roll tablespoons of mixture into 25 meatballs.

3 Lightly spray a large non-stick frying pan with oil and heat over medium–high heat. Cook meatballs for 2–3 minutes, turning, until browned. Transfer to prepared tray. Bake for 7–8 minutes or until meatballs are cooked through.

Anna's tip
This snack box is even more delicious with my Homemade tzatziki on page 67.

SCHOOL SNACK BOX

6 Homemade chicken nuggets

6 **3** **3**   SmartPoints value per serve

+

1 serve Creamy hummus

1 **0** **0**   SmartPoints value per serve

recipe page 66

+

cherry tomatoes and baby cucumbers

+

grapes and strawberries

Homemade chicken nuggets

serves 4   prep 15 min   cook 25 min

6 **3** **3**   SmartPoints value per serve

I don't know anyone that does not like a good chicken nugget! The best thing about these is that they are quick to make, using only four ingredients – always a win in my eyes.

2 eggs
500 g skinless chicken breasts, cut into 3 cm cubes
¾ cup (105 g) panko breadcrumbs
1 tablespoon Tuscan seasoning

1 Preheat oven to 200°C. Line a baking tray with baking paper.

2 Whisk eggs in a shallow bowl, then add all the chicken cubes and stir to coat. Combine breadcrumbs and Tuscan seasoning in a separate shallow bowl. Season with salt and pepper. Add half the chicken and toss to combine. Transfer to a plate. Repeat with remaining chicken.

3 Place nuggets on prepared tray and lightly spray with oil. Bake for 20–25 minutes or until golden and cooked through.

Anna's tip

You can also cook nuggets in an airfryer (200°C) in batches for 9 minutes or until golden.

WORK SNACK BOX

3 Chicken, spinach & feta patties

5 **3** **3** SmartPoints value per serve

+

3 tablespoons French onion dip

1 **0** **0** SmartPoints value per serve

recipe page 67

+

2 Mocha maple bliss balls

2 **2** **1** SmartPoints value per serve

recipe page 60

+

10 cashews

3 **3** **3** SmartPoints value per serve

+

2 x 15 g slices Jarlsberg lite cheese

2 **2** **2** SmartPoints value per serve

+

celery sticks

+

strawberries and blueberries

Chicken, spinach & feta patties

serves 4   prep 10 min   cook 10 min

5 **3** **3** SmartPoints value per serve

I often do a batch of these when visitors come over – they make lovely pre-dinner nibbles.

400 g chicken breast mince
1 egg, lightly beaten
250 g cooked spinach, drained and chopped (see tips)
½ cup (70 g) panko breadcrumbs
50 g reduced-fat feta cheese, crumbled
2 tablespoons light sweet chilli sauce (see tips)
2 teaspoons mixed dried herbs
2 tablespoons chopped flat-leaf parsley
1 teaspoon dried chilli flakes
1 small garlic clove, crushed

1 Combine mince, egg, spinach, breadcrumbs, feta, sweet chilli sauce, dried herbs, parsley, chilli flakes and garlic in a large bowl. Season with salt and pepper. Shape mixture into 12 patties.

2 Lightly spray a large non-stick frying pan with oil and heat over medium heat. Cook patties for 2–3 minutes each side or until golden and cooked through. Serve with extra sweet chilli sauce (see tips).

Anna's tips

* You can use thawed frozen spinach – just make sure you squeeze out any excess water.
* Serve with 3 tablespoons light sweet chilli sauce for dipping at no extra SmartPoints.

VEGETARIAN SNACK BOX

3 Beetroot falafel

9 **1** **1**   SmartPoints value per serve

+

3 tablespoons Homemade tzatziki

1 **0** **0**   SmartPoints value per serve

recipe page 67

+

2 Cherry ripe bliss balls

2 **2** **1**   SmartPoints value per serve

recipe page 60

+

10 dry-roasted almonds

2 **2** **2**   SmartPoints value per serve

+

sliced cucumber, carrot and radish

+

raspberries

Beetroot falafel

serves 4 prep 20 min   cook 1 hour 10 min

9 **1** **1**   SmartPoints value per serve

I absolutely love falafel, and my beetroot ones are by far my favourite. The flavours go so very well together, making these extremely moreish.

300 g dried chickpeas
150 g baby beetroot, unpeeled
1 garlic clove, crushed
1 tablespoon plain flour
1 teaspoon grated lemon zest
1 cup chopped flat-leaf parsley leaves
½ red onion, chopped
¼ teaspoon chilli flakes
½ teaspoon sumac

1 Place chickpeas in a large bowl. Cover well with cold water. Cover, set aside to soak overnight. Drain.

2 Preheat oven to 180°C. Line two baking trays with baking paper.

3 Cut beetroot in half and wrap in foil. Place on one baking tray and bake for 35–40 minutes or until cooked when pierced with a skewer. Cool, then peel off skins.

4 Place soaked chickpeas in a food processor with garlic, flour, zest, parsley, onion, chilli flakes and sumac. Pulse until chunky. Add beetroot and pulse again just enough for mixture to stick together.

5 Using an ice-cream scoop dipped in water, scoop mixture into your hand to shape into a falafel. Place on remaining baking tray. Repeat to make 12 falafels. Lightly spray with oil and place in the oven and bake for 30 minutes.

> **"Light lunches for home, work and school."**

Lunch

I like my lunch to be a balance of
protein, healthy carbs and loads of veg.
Most of these recipes can be prepared
the day before to be enjoyed as a
packed lunch for work or school,
or a relaxed meal at home.

Open Greek-style burger

serves 4   prep 15 min   cook 20 min

    SmartPoints value per serve

I turned my Greek mini meatballs recipe on page 74 into Greek-style burgers and they were a hit with everyone. Can you believe that these open burgers are so low in SmartPoints? Proving yet again that you certainly don't need to starve on WW.

2 teaspoons olive oil
1 red capsicum, cut into strips
1 yellow capsicum, cut into strips
½ cup (120 g) 99% fat-free plain yoghurt
1 tablespoon chopped flat-leaf parsley
1 teaspoon finely grated lemon zest
2 x 65 g wholemeal English muffins, split in half
1 garlic clove, cut in half
½ cup (15 g) baby rocket leaves
½ cup (10 g) baby spinach leaves

Burger
500 g chicken breast mince
1 red onion, finely diced
¼ cup chopped flat-leaf parsley
1 tablespoon finely chopped mint
1 teaspoon dried oregano
2 garlic cloves, grated
1 teaspoon finely grated lemon zest

1 Preheat oven to 180°C. Line a baking tray with baking paper. Combine all burger ingredients in a large bowl. Shape mixture into four 2 cm thick burger patties.

2 Heat oil in a large non-stick frying pan over high heat. Cook patties and capsicum for 5 minutes each side or until browned. Transfer patties and capsicum to prepared tray. Bake for 10–15 minutes or until cooked through.

3 Meanwhile, combine yoghurt, parsley and zest in a small bowl. Season with salt and pepper. Toast muffins then rub with cut side of garlic clove. Top each muffin half with rocket, spinach, a patty and capsicum. Dollop with yoghurt mixture, season with black pepper and serve.

Anna's tip
Uncooked patties can be frozen for up to 1 month.

50% **Weight Lost** | 100% **Healthier**

Crunchy slaw with chicken & sesame peanut dressing

serves 4   prep 15 min   cook 10 min

  SmartPoints value per serve

The crunchy texture of this salad with the tangy dressing is just spot on. Throw in some chicken for protein and this, my friends, makes a truly delicious lunch.

560 g small skinless chicken breasts (grilled, poached or steamed), shredded
½ wombok (Chinese cabbage), shredded
½ red cabbage, shredded
2 carrots, cut into matchsticks
2 pink lady apples, cut into matchsticks
1 small red onion, thinly sliced
½ cup shredded mint
1 cup (45 g) frozen podded edamame, thawed
1 teaspoon black sesame seeds (see tip)

Dressing
1 tablespoon natural smooth peanut butter
1 tablespoon soy sauce
2 teaspoons rice wine vinegar
2 teaspoons light sweet chilli sauce
2 teaspoons sesame oil
½ teaspoon finely grated ginger

1 To make dressing, whisk all ingredients in a small bowl until well combined.

2 Combine chicken, wombok, cabbage, carrot, apple, onion, mint and edamame in a large bowl. Add dressing and gently toss to combine. Serve sprinkled with black sesame seeds.

Anna's tip
You can find black sesame seeds in Asian grocery stores.

Chicken Caesar salad

serves 1   prep 10 min   cook 10 min

 SmartPoints value per serve

In most cafes, Caesar salads are ridiculously high in SmartPoints: up to 18 in some cases. Mine's much lower, and just as delicious.

2 cups (120 g) torn cos lettuce leaves
125 g grilled skinless chicken breast, sliced
1 x 25 g slice short-cut bacon, fat trimmed, diced
15 g bagel bites
10 g shaved parmesan cheese
1 hard-boiled egg, halved

Dressing
1 tablespoon 99% fat-free plain yoghurt
½ teaspoon wholegrain honey mustard
⅓ garlic clove, grated
1–2 teaspoons lemon juice

1 Heat a small non-stick frying pan over high heat. Cook bacon for 2 minutes or until golden and crisp.

2 To make dressing, combine all ingredients in a small bowl.

3 Combine lettuce, chicken, bacon, bagel bites, parmesan and egg in a bowl. Drizzle with dressing to serve.

Anna's tip
You can add anchovies or avocado for extra SmartPoints.

50% **Weight Lost** | 100% **Healthier**

Seriously good steak sandwich

serves 1   prep 10 min   cook 15 min

 SmartPoints value per serve

Caramelised onions, steak and egg squished between lightly toasted bread with garlic aioli ... This is my mouthwatering yet healthy take on a classic!

2 tablespoons 99% fat-free
   plain yoghurt
½ garlic clove, grated
1 teaspoon Dijon mustard
pinch herb salt
1 onion, thinly sliced
100 g lean sizzle or minute steak
1 egg
1 x 40 g sandwich thin,
   split in half and toasted
1 iceberg lettuce leaf
2 slices tomato

1 Combine yoghurt, garlic and mustard in a small bowl. Season with herb salt and black pepper. Set aside.

2 Meanwhile, line a medium non-stick frying pan with a pan liner (see tip) and heat over low heat. Cook onion, stirring occasionally, for 10 minutes or until golden. Transfer onion to a plate. Cover with foil to keep warm.

3 Increase heat to high. Season steak with salt and pepper. Cook steak for 1 minute each side or until cooked to your liking. Transfer steak to plate with onion. Pan-fry egg in same pan until cooked to your liking.

4 Cut steak in half. To serve, spread yoghurt aioli over slices of toast. Top base of sandwich with lettuce, tomato, steak, onion and egg. Top with other slice.

Anna's tip
WW reusable pan liners
are available to
purchase online

Tomato bruschetta

serves 1   prep 5 min   cook 5 min

 SmartPoints value per serve

Being Italian, I love my bruschetta. This is not the traditional way of eating it, but it's a variation I enjoy, and the feta is an added bonus.

**2 x 20 g slices ciabatta
   bread, toasted**
½ garlic clove
**125 g yellow and red cherry
   tomatoes, quartered**
¼ small red onion, finely diced
**1½ teaspoons garlic infused or
   extra-virgin olive oil**
**1 tablespoon shredded basil,
   plus extra leaves to serve**
5 g reduced-fat feta cheese
1 tablespoon balsamic glaze

1 Rub slices of toast with cut side of garlic clove. Combine tomato, onion, oil and basil in a small bowl. Season with salt and pepper.

2 Top toast with tomato mixture, crumble over feta and drizzle with balsamic glaze. Sprinkle with extra basil leaves to serve.

Cheesy chickpea & sweetcorn fritters

serves 4   prep 15 min   cook 15 min

 SmartPoints value per serve

My gosh, these vegie fritters are tasty! They're perfect for a delicious savoury breakfast as well as lunch. Enjoy!

400 g can chickpeas, drained and rinsed
120 g self-raising flour
2 eggs
¼ cup (60 ml) unsweetened almond milk
1 carrot, grated
½ small onion, diced
⅓ cup (80 g) 97% fat-free cottage cheese
1 tablespoon MasterFoods roast vegetable sprinkle (see tips)
¼ cup chopped flat-leaf parsley, plus extra to serve
1 cup (200 g) fresh corn kernels (see tips)
lemon wedges, to serve

Chilli dipping sauce
1 tablespoon light sweet chilli sauce
100 g 99% fat-free plain yoghurt

1   Process chickpeas, flour, eggs, milk, carrot, onion, cottage cheese, vegetable sprinkle and parsley in a food processor until smooth. Add corn and pulse until well combined, keeping some texture.

2   Heat a large non-stick frying pan over medium–high heat. Drop ¼ cup (60 ml) amounts of batter into pan to make 4 fritters. Cook for 3 minutes each side or until golden and cooked through. Repeat to make 12 fritters in total.

3   Meanwhile, combine sweet chilli sauce and yoghurt in a small bowl. Sprinkle the fritters with a bit more parsley and serve with chilli dipping sauce and lemon wedges on the side.

Anna's tips

✱ The roast vegetable sprinkle is readily available from all large supermarkets in the herb and spices section.

✱ You can use frozen kernels or rinsed and drained canned kernels instead of fresh, if you like.

Portuguese chicken burrito bowl

serves 1 prep 15 min cook 10 min

 SmartPoints value per serve

Burrito bowls are one of my family's favourite takeaway meals. This one leaves you feeling great, rather than heavy. The seasoning here has a little bit of spice but not too much; just enough to wake the tastebuds.

100 g skinless chicken breast

1 teaspoon Portuguese seasoning

1 cup (60 g) shredded iceberg lettuce

⅓ cup (70 g) cooked basmati rice

¼ small avocado (25 g), sliced

⅓ cup (55 g) drained and rinsed canned corn kernels

⅓ cup (65 g) drained and rinsed canned red kidney beans

⅓ cup (50 g) quartered cherry tomatoes

lime wedges, to serve

1 Rub chicken with seasoning. Heat a non-stick chargrill pan over medium heat. Cook chicken for 5 minutes each side or until golden and cooked through. Thinly slice chicken.

2 Place lettuce in a serving bowl. Top with rice, avocado, corn, beans, tomatoes and chicken. Serve with lime wedges.

Anna's tip

You can swap the rice for a light wrap for similar SmartPoints value.

Cheesy rice slice

serves 6 prep 15 min cook 40 min

 SmartPoints value per serve

I love this throw-together slice. Combine some leftover cooked rice and those vegies lurking in the crisper with some eggs and cheese and you have a delicious meal for very little effort.

1½ cups (255 g) cooked brown rice (see tips)

3 eggs, lightly beaten

2 teaspoons garlic-infused or extra-virgin olive oil

2 tablespoons grated parmesan cheese

½ cup (60 g) grated reduced-fat cheddar cheese

1 red onion, finely chopped

1 zucchini, grated

1 teaspoon Tuscan seasoning

1 Preheat oven to 180°C. Combine rice, egg, oil, cheeses, onion, zucchini and Tuscan seasoning in a large bowl. Season with salt and pepper.

2 Place a 13 cm x 15 cm (3 cm deep) silicone mould on a baking tray. Pour mixture into mould and smooth surface with the back of a spoon. Bake for 35–40 minutes or until golden and just firm, then serve.

Anna's tips

* Brown rice will keep you fuller for longer, but you can use white rice instead if that's what you have.

* I always meal prep a batch of rice at the beginning of the week so it's super quick and easy to pop into recipes like these.

Sweet chilli chicken & rice bowl

serves 1   prep 10 min   cook 10 min

 SmartPoints value per serve

Lunch bowls are my favourite midday meal. Healthy and filling, they take so little time to make. This one is just like a bowl of sunshine!

**1 tablespoon light sweet
  chilli sauce**
1 tablespoon soy sauce
1 garlic clove, crushed
240 g chicken tenderloins
**½ cup (100 g) cooked
  basmati rice**
**2 cups (190 g) shredded wombok
  (Chinese cabbage), steamed**
**½ cup (85 g) diced cooked
  pumpkin (see tip)**
4 cherry tomatoes, halved
½ teaspoon black sesame seeds
**1 tablespoon chopped
  flat-leaf parsley**

1   Combine sweet chilli sauce, soy sauce and garlic in a shallow dish. Add chicken and turn to coat. Cover and set aside for 5 minutes.

2   Heat a medium non-stick frying pan over medium heat (use a WW pan liner if desired). Cook chicken 5 minutes each side or until golden and cooked through. Transfer chicken to a plate. Cover with foil and set aside to rest for 5 minutes.

3   Arrange chicken, rice, cabbage, pumpkin and tomato in a serving bowl. Sprinkle with sesame seeds and parsley to serve.

Anna's tip

You can roast, boil, steam or microwave diced pumpkin until tender. Roasted pumpkin tastes the best. I usually make extra for dinner so I can use it in lunches.

Sticky barbecue glazed meatballs

serves 4   prep 15 min   cook 10 min

 SmartPoints value per serve

Well, these are just absolutely delightful mouthfuls of flavour! They are on permanent rotation in our house, and I often pack them in a lunch jar with my vegetarian rice filling (page 136) and baby spinach leaves. They make a great party snack, too.

500 g chicken breast mince

1 small onion, finely chopped

¼ cup finely chopped flat-leaf parsley

3 teaspoons all-purpose seasoning

1 teaspoon sesame seeds, toasted

4 cups (120 g) salad leaves

lemon wedges, to serve

Sticky barbecue glaze

1 tablespoon Worcestershire sauce

1 tablespoon apple cider vinegar (see tip)

2 tablespoons chicken stock

2½ tablespoons no-added-sugar barbecue sauce

1 Combine chicken, onion, parsley and all-purpose seasoning in a medium bowl. Season with salt and pepper. Shape rounded tablespoons of mixture into 24 meatballs.

2 Heat a large non-stick frying pan over medium heat. Cook meatballs, in batches if necessary, turning for 5 minutes or until just browned.

3 Meanwhile, to make the glaze, combine Worcestershire sauce, vinegar, stock and barbecue sauce in a medium saucepan over medium heat. Season with salt and pepper. Bring to the boil. Add meatballs, reduce heat and simmer for 5 minutes, stirring occasionally, until liquid has reduced to a sticky thick glaze and meatballs are cooked through. Sprinkle with sesame seeds and serve with salad leaves and lemon wedges.

Anna's tip

Look for apple cider vinegar in the health-food section of the supermarket.

Open chicken, bacon & poached egg sandwich

serves 2   prep 10 min   cook 10 min

 SmartPoints value per serve

My take on a Caesar sandwich! Heaven on a plate. Just look at that egg …

2 tablespoons 99% fat-free plain yoghurt

1 teaspoon honey wholegrain mustard

1 x 200 g skinless chicken breast, halved horizontally

4 x 25 g slices short-cut bacon, fat trimmed

2 eggs (see tip)

½ teaspoon white vinegar

2 slices (2 x 40 g) sourdough bread, toasted

½ garlic clove

1 cup (30 g) rocket leaves

1 Combine yoghurt and mustard in a small bowl. Set aside.

2 Lightly spray a large non-stick chargrill pan with oil and heat over medium heat. Cook chicken and bacon for 5 minutes each side or until golden and cooked through.

3 Meanwhile, to poach eggs, fill a medium deep-frying pan three-quarters with water, add vinegar and bring to the boil, reduce to a simmer. Carefully break 1 egg into a cup, then slide into simmering water. Repeat with remaining egg. Poach eggs gently for 1–2 minutes, or until egg whites are set and yolks are still soft. Cook a minute or two longer if you like your yolk firm.

4 Rub toast with cut side of garlic clove. Place toast onto serving plates. Top each slice with rocket, chicken, bacon and egg. Drizzle with dressing and season with salt and pepper to serve.

Anna's tip

I find that the freshest eggs are always best for poaching.

Pork & mushroom larb lettuce wraps

serves 4   prep 15 min   cook 10 min

 SmartPoints value per serve

This is a SmartPoints-friendly version of one of my favourite takeaway meals. Although it is not authentic, the flavours are really delicious ... plus I can enjoy it anytime!

1 small red onion, finely chopped

500 g lean pork mince

500 g button mushrooms, sliced

1 red capsicum, finely chopped

150 g corn kernels

3 garlic cloves, grated

4 green shallots, thinly sliced

1 tablespoon soy sauce

2 teaspoons fish sauce

**1 tablespoon light sweet
chilli sauce**

1 teaspoon finely grated lime zest

1 tablespoon lime juice

1 teaspoon dried chilli flakes

**2 baby cos lettuces,
leaves separated**

1 Lightly spray a wok with oil. Heat over a high heat for 20 seconds, stir-fry red onion and pork for 5 minutes, breaking up lumps as it cooks. Add mushrooms, capsicum, corn, garlic, three-quarters of the shallots, soy sauce, fish sauce, sweet chilli sauce, zest, juice and chilli. Stir-fry for 3 minutes or until liquid is evaporated.

2 Serve in lettuce leaves scattered with remaining shallots.

50% **Weight Lost** | 100% **Healthier**

Creamy pumpkin & maple soup

serves 8   prep 10 min   cook 3 hrs 20 min

 SmartPoints value per serve

Pumpkin soup is one of our favourite soups in winter. I use Kent pumpkin because of its nutty flavour. Adding maple syrup takes its sweetness to the next level – yum.

1 large Kent pumpkin (3 kg)
2 onions, chopped
4 celery sticks, chopped
3 carrots, chopped
3 garlic cloves, crushed
400 g can diced tomatoes
2 teaspoons dried mixed herbs
1.5 litres (6 cups) chicken stock
⅓ cup (80 ml) sugar-free
**   maple syrup**
2 tablespoons light cream

1 Preheat oven to 200°C. Wrap whole pumpkin in foil with foil joining at the top so it's easy to open (see tip). Place in oven and bake for 2½ hours, then open up foil to uncover pumpkin and bake for a further 20 minutes or until pumpkin is tender. Set aside to cool. Cut pumpkin in half and scoop out and discard seeds. Scoop out flesh and set aside.

2 Lightly spray a large saucepan with oil and heat over medium heat. Cook onion, celery, carrot and garlic, stirring, for 5 minutes or until softened. Add tomato, herbs, reserved pumpkin flesh and stock. Add a little more water if needed to cover top of vegetables. Season with salt and pepper. Bring to the boil, then reduce heat and simmer, uncovered, for 20 minutes or until vegetables are soft.

3 Using a food processor or stick blender, process soup until smooth. Return soup to medium heat. Add maple syrup and cream and cook, stirring, until heated through. Serve straight away.

Anna's tip

Alternatively, cut the pumpkin in half and wrap each half in foil with foil joining at the top. Bake for 1 hour, or until pumpkin is tender.

Cauliflower & pear soup

serves 2   prep 5 min   cook 15 min

   SmartPoints value per serve

I've never revealed to my family the secret ingredient that makes this soup so tasty and moreish, but I am now sharing it with everyone! Adding pear (yes, pear!) brings such a sweet depth of flavour. Once you try it, I promise you'll make it again.

310 ml (1¼ cups) chicken stock
400 g cauliflower, cut into florets
2 pears, peeled and chopped
1 tablespoon 99% fat-free
**   plain yoghurt**
1 teaspoon flaked almonds,
**   toasted**
1 teaspoon sugar-free
**   maple syrup**

1 Place stock, cauliflower and pear in a medium saucepan over medium–high heat. Bring to the boil then reduce heat and simmer, uncovered, for 10 minutes or until pear and cauliflower are tender.

2 Using a food processor or stick blender, process soup until smooth. Season with salt and pepper. Return soup to medium heat and cook, stirring, until heated through. Serve topped with yoghurt, almonds and maple syrup.

BLT with garlic herb dressing

serves 1   prep 5 min   cook 5 min

 SmartPoints value per serve

There's absolutely no need to miss out on your favourite foods while you're losing or maintaining weight! This sandwich is a perfect example. I mean, c'mon: YUM!! And it takes just 10 minutes to make. Here's how …

50 g 99% fat-free plain yoghurt

1 teaspoon finely chopped flat-leaf parsley

1 teaspoon finely chopped basil

½ garlic clove, grated

2 x 25 g slices short-cut bacon, fat trimmed

50 g butternut pumpkin, peeled and cut into 1–2 mm slices

2 x 27 g slices spelt bread, toasted

2 iceberg lettuce leaves

3 slices tomato

1 tablespoon thinly sliced red onion

1 stuffed green olive (optional)

1   To make the dressing, combine yoghurt, parsley, basil and garlic in a small bowl. Season with salt and pepper.

2   Heat a large non-stick frying pan over medium heat. Cook bacon and pumpkin slices for 2 minutes each side or until golden.

3   Spread dressing on one side of each piece of toast. Layer one slice with lettuce, bacon, pumpkin, tomato and onion. Season with salt and pepper. Enclose sandwich with remaining dressed toast.

4   Skewer a stuffed olive with a toothpick, if using. Spear one of the sandwich halves and serve.

Anna's tip

I LOVE iceberg lettuce, even if it's not very fashionable! Its delicious crispness is amazing in sandwiches. Give it a go!

Edible crunchy wrap bowl

serves 1   prep 10 min   cook 15 min

  SmartPoints value per serve

Ah, it is extremely satisfying to crunch on this lunch. You can fill the bowl with the protein and vegies of your choice – get creative and have some fun.

1 x 43 g light white wrap
1 x 125 g skinless chicken breast
1 tablespoon light sweet
   chilli sauce
1 garlic clove, crushed
½ cup (100 g) corn kernels
1 cup (60 g) shredded iceberg
   lettuce
½ Lebanese cucumber, sliced
1 small tomato, finely chopped
1 tablespoon finely chopped
   red onion
½ cup (90 g) drained and rinsed
   canned black beans
1 tablespoon 99% fat-free
   plain yoghurt
20 g avocado, sliced
flat-leaf parsley or coriander
   leaves, to serve
lemon wedge, to serve

1   Preheat oven to 200°C. Press wrap into an ovenproof bowl (no need to spray with oil) or tortilla tin. Bake for 10–15 minutes or until golden, checking occasionally to ensure it doesn't burn. Remove from bowl or tin and allow to cool completely.

2   Meanwhile, combine chicken, sweet chilli sauce and garlic in a shallow dish. Heat a non-stick chargrill pan or frying pan over medium heat. Cook chicken for 5 minutes each side or until golden and cooked through. Cook corn for 2 minutes or until slightly charred. Transfer to a plate.

3   Slice chicken or cut into chunks. Fill wrap bowl with lettuce, chicken, corn, cucumber, tomato, onion and beans. Top with yoghurt, avocado and herbs. Serve with lemon wedge.

Slow-cooker pea & ham soup

serves 6 prep 10 min cook 6–8 hours

 SmartPoints value per serve

It doesn't matter how delicious pea and ham soup is, you just can't make it look pretty. Luckily, it's all about the taste! This is my amazingly easy slow-cooker recipe.

1½ cups (315 g) green split peas
1 small onion, diced
2 celery sticks, diced
1 large carrot, diced
2 garlic cloves, grated
3 cups (750 ml) chicken stock
2 bay leaves
400 g loin ham, fat trimmed,
** diced**
1½ cups (180 g) frozen peas

1 Place split peas, onion, celery, carrot, garlic, stock, bay leaves, ham and 1 cup (250 ml) water in a 4.5 litre (18-cup) capacity slow-cooker.

2 Cook, covered, on low for 6–8 hours (or high for 4–5 hours) or until peas are cooked and soup is thick. Add frozen peas and cook for 10 minutes or until peas are tender. Serve.

50% **Weight Lost** | 100% **Healthier**

Portuguese chicken burger

serves 1   prep 5 min   cook 10 min

 SmartPoints value per serve

I absolutely love the flavours of Nando's chicken, especially the burgers. So, here I've recreated one of my favourite dishes. Now I can enjoy those Portuguese flavours guilt-free more often.

1 x 125 g skinless chicken breast
1 teaspoon Portuguese seasoning
1 tablespoon 99% fat-free plain yoghurt
½ teaspoon Nando's hot sauce (or mild if you prefer)
1 x 50 g brioche bun, split, toasted (see tip)
1 iceberg lettuce leaf
2 slices tomato

1 Rub chicken all over with seasoning. Heat a non-stick chargrill pan over medium heat. Cook chicken for 4–5 minutes each side, or until golden and cooked through.

2 Combine yoghurt and hot sauce in a small bowl.

3 To assemble, top bun base with lettuce, chicken, yoghurt dressing and tomato. Enclose with bun lid.

Anna's tip

Add 1 x 17 g slice reduced-fat cheddar cheese for 1 extra SmartPoints value per serve. Melt cheese on toasted bun base under a hot grill for 1–2 minutes.

Nonna's chicken soup

serves 4   prep 15 min   cook 35 min

  SmartPoints value per serve

My beautiful grandmother used to cook this soup for us, as children and as adults. It remains one of my favourite comfort meals for a cosy winter's lunch.

200 g potato, peeled and diced
1 tomato, chopped
3 carrots, chopped
2 celery sticks, chopped
1 small onion, finely chopped
1 litre (4 cups) chicken stock
250 g cooked skinless chicken breast, shredded
400 g can butter beans, drained and rinsed
⅓ cup chopped flat-leaf parsley, plus extra leaves to garnish

1 Lightly spray a large saucepan with oil and heat over medium heat. Cook potato, tomato, carrot, celery and onion, stirring, for 10 minutes or until vegetables start to soften. Season with salt and pepper.

2 Add stock and bring to the boil, then reduce heat and simmer, uncovered, for 20 minutes or until vegetables are tender. Add chicken, beans and parsley. Simmer for 2–3 minutes or until heated through. Serve sprinkled with extra parsley and season with black pepper.

Salmon buddha bowl

serves 1   prep 10 min   cook 10 min

8 **1** **0**   **SmartPoints value per serve**

A filling and nourishing bowl of goodness. If you haven't tried this edamame spaghetti, give it a go – oh my gosh, it is absolutely delicious! You'll find it in the health-food section of larger supermarkets.

50 g edamame bean spaghetti
½ cup (75 g) diced pumpkin
½ cup (60 g) frozen peas
50 g skinless salmon fillet
  (or canned salmon)
1 cup (20 g) baby spinach leaves
1 hard-boiled egg, halved
6 grape tomatoes, halved
125 g can chickpeas, drained
  and rinsed
½ teaspoon black sesame seeds

1 Cook spaghetti in a saucepan of boiling salted water, following packet instructions. Drain.

2 Meanwhile, steam pumpkin, peas and salmon until vegetables are tender and salmon is cooked to your liking. Drain. Season vegetables with salt and pepper.

3 Arrange spinach, pasta, steamed vegetables, egg, tomatoes and chickpeas in a bowl. Flake salmon and add to bowl. Serve sprinkled with sesame seeds.

"Special
meals for all
occasions."

Entertaining

Cooking for family and friends brings
me so much joy. There is nothing better
than being with people I love, sharing good
food and making memories. Here, I'm
sharing the simple crowd-pleasing recipes
I make for birthdays, barbecues
and special meals.

Entertaining menu

STARTERS

Pork, apple & thyme sausage rolls
Cheesy asparagus with prosciutto

SIDES

Barbecued veg, quinoa & feta salad
Spinach & cashew salad
Mango salad with citrus dressing

MAINS

Lamb with pumpkin & couscous salad
Lemon, herb & garlic chicken

DESSERTS

Tiramisu cake
Cinnamon apple tartlets

Pork, apple & thyme sausage rolls

makes 24   prep 20 min   cook 30 min

 SmartPoints value per roll

Fabulous for party treats, these are so delicious and contain much less fat than regular sausage rolls. You can prepare them in advance and freeze them, then simply bake on the day.

500 g extra-lean pork mince
3 apples, grated
1 x 35 g slice high-fibre white bread,
   made into breadcrumbs
1 egg
½ onion, finely diced
2 teaspoons chopped thyme leaves
6 sheets filo pastry
2 tablespoons sesame
   seeds

1 Preheat oven to 200°C. Line two baking trays with baking paper.

2 Combine mince, apple, breadcrumbs, egg, onion and thyme in a large bowl. Season with salt and pepper.

3 Lightly spray 1 filo sheet with oil. Top with another sheet. Spoon one-third of the pork mixture along the long edge. Brush edges of pastry with a little water and roll to enclose filling. Cut log into 8 pieces and transfer to prepared tray. Repeat with remaining filo sheets and filling to make 24 sausage rolls.

4 Spray rolls lightly with oil and sprinkle with sesame seeds. Bake for 25–30 minutes, swapping trays halfway through cooking time, or until golden and cooked through.

Cheesy asparagus with prosciutto

serves 4   prep 10 min   cook 20 min

 SmartPoints value per serve

This starter is really simple, yet packs a ton of flavour. Melted cheese is always a winner in my eyes, especially with prosciutto! I love using garlic-infused olive oil. Just a drizzle can liven up a dish and it's so easy and convenient.

4 bunches asparagus
2 teaspoons garlic-infused olive oil
½ cup (60 g) grated reduced-fat mozzarella cheese
65 g prosciutto, fat trimmed, diced

1 Preheat oven to 180°C. Lay asparagus spears on a baking tray. Drizzle with olive oil, season with salt and pepper and scatter over cheese and prosciutto. Season with a little more pepper.

2 Bake asparagus for 15–20 minutes or until cheese is melted and prosciutto is crisp. Serve.

Anna's tip
You can use poppy seeds instead of sesame seeds for the same SmartPoints value.

Barbecued veg, quinoa & feta salad

serves 6   prep 20 min   cook 10 min

 SmartPoints value per serve

Cooking vegetables on the barbecue gives them a completely different flavour to roasting, and it's also the easiest way of cooking a decent amount all at once – perfect for when you're entertaining. I like to combine all the cooked components when they're warm, then let the salad cool to really meld all the flavours together.

1 red capsicum,
   cut into thick slices
1 yellow capsicum,
   cut into thick slices
1 orange capsicum,
   cut into thick slices
4 baby zucchini, cut into
   thick wedges lengthways
4 baby eggplant, cut into
   thick wedges lengthways
½ small butternut pumpkin,
   cut into 1 cm thick batons
1 tablespoon garlic-infused
   olive oil
1 tablespoon mixed dried herbs
2 cups (400 g) cooked quinoa
1 cup chopped flat-leaf parsley
1 tablespoon red wine vinegar
30 g reduced-fat Greek feta
   cheese, crumbled

1   Combine capsicums, zucchini, eggplant and pumpkin in a shallow dish. Add oil and dried herbs and season with salt and pepper. Toss until well combined.

2   Preheat a chargrill or barbecue over medium-high heat. Cook vegetables, turning, for 5–7 minutes or until golden and tender.

3   Combine quinoa, grilled vegetables and parsley in a large bowl. Drizzle with vinegar and season with salt and pepper. Gently toss to combine. Serve sprinkled with feta.

Anna's tip

I prep a batch of quinoa at the beginning of the week so it's super easy to quickly bulk up my salads.

50% **Weight Lost** | 100% **Healthier**

**MANGO SALAD WITH
CITRUS DRESSING**

page 122

**SPINACH &
CASHEW SALAD**

page 122

**LAMB
WITH PUMPKIN &
COUSCOUS SALAD**
page 123

Spinach & cashew salad

serves 4   prep 10 min

3 **3** **3**   SmartPoints value per serve

There is nothing more refreshing than seasonal fruit in a salad. With its vibrant colours, this looks amazing, too. Increase quantities to serve a crowd.

120 g baby spinach leaves
1–2 handfuls bean sprouts
1 large mango, sliced
½ cup mint leaves
1 Lebanese cucumber, sliced
30 g unsalted cashew nuts
½ pomegranate
1 tablespoon lime juice
2 teaspoons sesame oil
1½ teaspoons black sesame seeds
lime wedges, to serve

1 Combine spinach, sprouts, mango, mint, cucumber and cashews in a large bowl. Working over a separate bowl, remove seeds from pomegranate carefully (see tip), catching any juice in the bowl. Set seeds aside.

2 Add lime juice and sesame oil to bowl with pomegranate juice and combine. Add dressing to salad and gently toss to combine. Season with salt and pepper. Sprinkle pomegranate seeds and sesame seeds over salad. Serve with lime wedges.

Anna's tip

To remove the seeds from a pomegranate, hold the fruit cut side down and gently tap all over with a rolling pin or meat mallet until the seeds fall into the bowl.

Mango salad with citrus dressing

serves 4   prep 10 min

2 **2** **2**   SmartPoints value per serve

I serve this fresh side salad with the chicken on page 124 for a beautiful summery meal. You could also add rice for a more substantial salad or for more guests.

500 g cherry tomatoes, halved
75 g reduced-fat feta cheese, diced
½ Lebanese cucumber, diced
½ red onion, diced
2 small mangoes, diced
¼ cup chopped mint
1 tablespoon orange juice
1 tablespoon lime juice

1 Combine tomato, feta, cucumber, onion, mango and mint in a large bowl. Add juices and gently toss to combine. Season with salt and pepper and serve.

50% **Weight Lost** | 100% **Healthier**

Lamb with pumpkin & couscous salad

serves 4   prep 15 min   cook 25 min

10 **8** **8**   **SmartPoints value per serve**

My favourite way to eat lamb is to barbecue it – the taste is just amazing.
The couscous salad features dates and chickpeas for a delicious Moroccan twist.
It is absolutely full of flavour and your guests will be begging you for the recipe!

**500 g Kent pumpkin, peeled
   and diced**
**4 x 150 g lamb leg steaks,
   fat trimmed**
**1 tablespoon lamb herb
   seasoning**
1 cup (190 g) couscous
**4 medjool dates, pitted
   and chopped**
1 red onion, diced
4 baby cucumbers, diced
⅔ cup (60 g) diced red capsicum
**400 g can chickpeas, drained
   and rinsed**
½ cup chopped flat-leaf parsley
**⅓ cup (80 ml) freshly squeezed
   orange juice**

1   Preheat oven to 200°C. Line a large baking tray with baking paper. Spread pumpkin over tray. Roast for 20 minutes or until tender and caramelised. Set aside.

2   Preheat a chargrill pan or barbecue over high heat. Sprinkle lamb with seasoning. Cook lamb for 2 minutes each side or until cooked to your liking. Transfer to a plate. Cover lamb with foil and set aside to rest for 3 minutes before thickly slicing.

3   Meanwhile, place couscous in a large heatproof bowl. Add 1 cup (250 ml) boiling water and season with salt. Stir, cover and set aside for 5 minutes or until water has absorbed. Scrape with a fork to separate grains.

4   Combine couscous, dates, onion, cucumber, capsicum, chickpeas, pumpkin and parsley in a large bowl. Add orange juice and gently toss to combine. Season with salt and pepper. Serve lamb with couscous salad.

Lemon, herb & garlic chicken

serves 4   prep 10 min + marinating   cook 20 min

 SmartPoints value per serve

I serve this amazing chicken dish with the mango salad on page 122. I love marinating my chicken overnight. This not only makes the chicken extra tasty, but also allows for easy cooking for the next day. Use it in salads and your snack boxes during the week.

2 teaspoons finely grated lemon zest
2 tablespoons lemon juice
¼ cup chopped thyme, plus extra to garnish
1 teaspoon dried oregano
3 garlic cloves, grated
2 teaspoons garlic-infused or extra-virgin olive oil
1 teaspoon Dijon mustard
1 teaspoon dried chilli flakes (optional)
500 g skinless chicken breast tenderloins or fillets
lemon wedges, to serve

1 Combine zest, juice, thyme, oregano, garlic, oil, mustard and chilli flakes (if using) in a large zip-lock bag. Add chicken and toss to coat. Cover and refrigerate for 30 minutes, or longer if you have time.

2 Heat a large non-stick frying pan over medium–high heat. Cook chicken, in batches, for 3–4 minutes on each side or until golden and cooked through.

3 Serve sprinkled with thyme, and lemon wedges for squeezing over.

50% **Weight Lost** | 100% **Healthier**

Tiramisu sponge cake

serves 12   prep 20 min   cook 25 min

5 **5** **5**   SmartPoints value per serve

A classic dessert made into a light sponge with the same coffee hit. Enjoy with friends or simply with a cup of espresso coffee for afternoon tea in true Italian tradition.

4 eggs, separated
130 g caster sugar
15 g finely ground coffee (see tip)
70 g plain flour
½ cup (60 g) custard powder
¾ cup (180 g) 99% fat-free plain yoghurt
200 g reduced-fat fresh ricotta cheese
1 teaspoon vanilla essence
30 ml coffee liqueur
1 teaspoon cocoa powder

1 Preheat oven to 170°C. Line base and sides of a 20 cm square cake tin with baking paper.

2 Using electric beaters, beat egg whites and a pinch of salt in a large bowl until frothy. Gradually add 30 g of the caster sugar, beating as you go, until firm peaks form. Set aside.

3 In a separate bowl, beat egg yolks, ground coffee and remaining sugar in a large bowl until thick and creamy. Using a large metal spoon, gently fold egg white mixture into egg yolk mixture, in two batches, until just combined.

4 Sift flour and custard powder into a bowl. Gently fold flour mixture into egg mixture, in 3 batches, until just combined. Pour mixture into prepared tin and smooth surface with the back of a spoon.

5 Bake for 20–25 minutes or until golden and a skewer inserted into the centre comes out clean. Set cake aside in tin for 5 minutes before transferring to a wire rack to cool completely.

6 Meanwhile, whisk yoghurt, ricotta, vanilla and liqueur in a medium bowl. Carefully cut cooled sponge in half horizontally. Spread base with half the ricotta mixture. Top with sponge layer and spread with remaining ricotta. Dust with cocoa powder and serve.

Anna's tip
I use ground coffee for an espresso machine.

50% **Weight Lost** | 100% **Healthier**

Cinnamon apple tartlets

makes 12   prep 10 min   cook 35 min

  SmartPoints value per tartlet

In these cute little bites, the juicy apple and sweet cinnamon pairs with the crisp crunch of the wonton base for a deliciously light way to end a meal.

2 pink lady apples (300 g), peeled and diced
1 teaspoon vanilla extract
1 teaspoon ground cinnamon, plus extra to serve
12 x 6 g wonton wrappers
1 egg, lightly beaten
1 teaspoon cinnamon sugar
½ cup (120 g) 99% fat-free plain yoghurt
mint leaves, to serve

1 Place apple, vanilla and cinnamon in a saucepan and cook, stirring occasionally, over a medium heat for 15–20 minutes or until tender. Set aside to cool slightly.

2 Meanwhile, preheat oven to 180°C. Brush wonton wrappers with beaten egg and sprinkle with a little cinnamon sugar. Place wrappers, cinnamon side up, in a 12-hole (1½ tablespoon capacity) mini-muffin silicone mould.

3 Bake tart cases for 10–15 minutes or until golden and crisp. Cool slightly. Spoon warm apple mixture into cases and serve topped with a dollop of yoghurt and sprinkled with extra cinnamon and mint leaves.

66
**Fuss-free
meals for
every family."**

Dinner

For my family, dinner is the meal where we all come together at the table to enjoy home-cooked food and each other's company. Healthy meals don't need to be complicated in order to be tasty. A few staple ingredients and lots of fresh produce can give you a delicious balanced meal in no time.

Dinner

Three-ingredient pizza dough with prosciutto, rocket & feta

serves 4   prep 20 min   cook 15 min

 SmartPoints value per serve

The latest food trend is making pizza dough with yoghurt. Well, being Italian, I do love my pizza, and I was doubtful this three-ingredient recipe could match the taste and texture of traditional yeast dough. But this is absolutely amazing! It works like magic with no compromise on taste and, best of all, it is so easy that anyone can do it.

1 cup (150 g) self-raising flour
1 teaspoon mixed dried herbs
1 cup (240 g) 99% fat-free
plain yoghurt
1 tablespoon polenta
⅓ cup (80 g) canned
diced tomato
50 g grated mozzarella cheese
4 x 12.5 g slices prosciutto,
fat trimmed
8 cherry tomatoes, halved
1 cup (30 g) baby rocket leaves
25 g reduced-fat feta
cheese, crumbled
8 basil leaves

1   Preheat oven to 200°C. Combine flour, dried herbs, ½ teaspoon salt and yoghurt in a medium bowl, stirring until a soft dough forms. Transfer dough to a lightly floured surface and knead for 5 minutes or until smooth.

2   Roll dough out between 2 sheets of baking paper, lightly dusted with flour, to approximately a 30 cm diameter circle. Sprinkle a large pizza tray with polenta. Peel top sheet of baking paper from dough and invert onto prepared tray. Peel remaining sheet of baking paper.

3   Spread diced tomato over base and sprinkle with mozzarella. Bake for 10–15 minutes or until golden and base is crisp. Serve topped with prosciutto, cherry tomatoes, rocket, feta and basil. Cut into slices to serve.

Dinner

Steak burgers in brioche

serves 1   prep 10 min   cook 5 min

  SmartPoints value per serve

This is so much healthier than the cafe-style steak burger that's a gazillion SmartPoints. And it's completely delicious, too.

1 ½ tablespoons 99% fat-free plain yoghurt
½ small garlic clove, grated
1 teaspoon Dijon mustard
100 g beef sizzle or minute steak
1 egg
1 x 54 g brioche bun, split and toasted
2 cups (60 g) mixed salad leaves, to serve
1 x 21 g slice reduced-fat cheddar cheese
1 small tomato, sliced
¼ small red onion, thinly sliced

1 Combine yoghurt, garlic and mustard in a small bowl. Season with salt and pepper.

2 Heat a medium non-stick frying pan over high heat and lightly spray with oil. Season steak with salt and pepper, and cook for 1 minute each side or until cooked to your liking. Transfer to a plate. Cover beef with foil and set aside to rest for 2 minutes. Meanwhile, fry egg in same pan until cooked to your liking.

3 Spread bun base with yoghurt mixture. Cut steak in half. Top with some salad leaves, cheddar, steak, tomato, onion and egg. Serve with remaining salad leaves on the side.

50% **Weight Lost** | 100% **Healthier**

Cheesy roasted butternut pumpkin with vegetable rice filling

serves 4   prep 20 min   cook 45 min

4 **4** **2**   SmartPoints value per serve

This dish works equally well as a main or a side served with some lean protein. My secret to making vegetables extra tasty is to use loads of herbs and spices that bring an abundance of flavour.

2 x 1.4 kg butternut pumpkins, halved
1 onion, finely chopped
1 yellow capsicum, diced
1 zucchini, diced
2 garlic cloves, grated
½ teaspoon dried chilli flakes
1 tablespoon thyme leaves
¼ cup chopped flat-leaf parsley, plus extra to serve
1 cup (170 g) cooked brown rice (see tip)
8 cherry tomatoes, halved
½ cup (60 g) grated mozzarella cheese

1 Preheat oven to 180°C, line a baking tray with baking paper.

2 Remove seeds from pumpkin. Cut out flesh, leaving a 2 cm border. Dice pumpkin flesh and place on prepared tray along with the 4 pumpkin halves, flesh side down. Lightly spray diced pumpkin with oil and season with salt and pepper. Bake for 30–35 minutes or until softened.

3 Meanwhile, heat a medium non-stick frying pan over medium heat. Cook onion, capsicum and zucchini, stirring, for 6–7 minutes or until softened. Add garlic, chilli flakes, thyme and parsley and cook, stirring, for 1–2 minutes or until fragrant. Season with salt and pepper.

4 Combine onion mixture, rice and diced roasted pumpkin in a large bowl. Turn pumpkin halves over and fill with rice mixture. Top each pumpkin half with 4 cherry tomato halves and sprinkle with mozzarella. Bake for 10 minutes or until cheese has melted and tomatoes are wilted. Sprinkle with extra parsley to serve.

Anna's tip
I meal prep a batch of brown rice so it's super easy to grab and add to delicious dishes like this one.

Chilli chicken tacos

serves 4   prep 20 min   cook 30 min

 SmartPoints value per serve

Tacos are one of my favourite throw-together 'fakeaway' meals and this quick and easy end-of-the-week version is always a winner. No packet mix here – just fresh ingredients with a simple homemade spice blend.

1 onion, finely chopped
500 g chicken breast mince
3 garlic cloves, grated
400 g can diced tomatoes
1 chicken stock cube, crumbled
400 g can black beans,
**   drained and rinsed**
125 g can corn kernels, drained
8 x 14 g taco shells, warmed
4 cups (240 g) shredded
**   iceberg lettuce**
12 cherry tomatoes, halved
⅓ cup (40 g) grated reduced-fat
**   cheddar cheese**

Homemade spice mix
1 teaspoon chilli powder
1 teaspoon dried mixed herbs
1 teaspoon mild paprika
½ teaspoon ground cinnamon
½ teaspoon allspice
½ teaspoon cocoa powder
½ teaspoon salt
½ teaspoon black pepper

1 To make homemade spice mix, combine all spice mix ingredients in a small bowl.

2 Lightly spray a large non-stick frying pan with oil and heat over medium–high heat. Cook onion, stirring, for 5 minutes or until softened. Add mince and garlic and cook, stirring to break up lumps, for 5 minutes or until browned. Add homemade spice mix and cook, stirring, for 2 minutes or until fragrant.

3 Add tomato, stock cube, beans, corn and ½ cup (125 ml) water, and bring to the boil. Reduce heat and simmer, partially covered, for 15–20 minutes or until thick.

4 Serve mince mixture in taco shells topped with lettuce, tomato and cheddar.

Crispy crunchy cornflake chicken

serves 4   prep 10 min   cook 30 min

 SmartPoints value per serve

There's nothing I love more than crunchy coated chicken, and I like to use cornflakes to get that extra-crunchy texture. I also like the chicken to have tenderness and flavour, so, before crumbing, I dredge the chicken in my fave mix of yoghurt and mustard. Add wedges and salad and it's the best meal around!

170 g 99% fat-free plain yoghurt
1 teaspoon Dijon mustard
½ garlic clove, grated
3 cups (120 g) cornflakes, crushed
2 x 250 g skinless chicken
**   breasts, halved horizontally**

1 Preheat oven to 180°C. Line a baking tray with baking paper.

2 Combine yoghurt, mustard and garlic in a shallow bowl. Season with salt and pepper. Place cornflakes in a separate shallow bowl. Working with 1 piece of chicken at a time, dip in yoghurt mixture to coat then toss in crumbs to coat.

3 Place chicken on prepared tray in a single layer and lightly spray with oil. Bake for 25–30 minutes or until golden and cooked through.

Anna's tip
You can also cook the chicken in an airfryer at 180°C for 12 minutes.

Corn, polenta & parmesan fritters

makes 10   prep 10 min   cook 15 min

 SmartPoints value per fritter

These are one of my Meatless Monday creations. I serve them with a lovely big salad, and they are also great to take along to a picnic or barbecue. Using polenta instead of flour gives them a bit more flavour and – bonus – also makes them gluten free.

2 cups (240 g) grated zucchini
¼ cup (20 g) finely grated
   parmesan cheese
½ cup (85 g) yellow polenta
2 corn cobs, kernels removed
2 teaspoons gluten-free
   baking powder
2 tablespoons chopped
   flat-leaf parsley
2 tablespoons chopped thyme
4 eggs, lightly beaten
2 teaspoons olive oil

1   Squeeze excess water from zucchini. Combine zucchini, parmesan, polenta, corn, baking powder, parsley, thyme and eggs in a large bowl. Season with salt and pepper.

2   Heat a large non-stick frying pan over medium–high heat. Brush pan with a little oil. Drop ¼ cup (60 ml) quantities of batter into pan to make 2–3 fritters. Cook for 2 minutes each side or until golden and cooked through. Repeat with remaining oil and batter to make a total of 10 fritters. Serve.

Slow-cooker Italian pork stew

serves 4   prep 15 min   cook 2 hour 20 min

 SmartPoints value per serve

I love my slow-cooker, especially when the cooler weather arrives. It saves me so much time and effort when I make stews like this one. I don't have to hover over the stove all evening, plus the slow-cooking really draws out all the wonderful flavours. This cut of pork is quite lean, so it only takes a couple of hours from start to finish.

850 g lean pork fillet,
** diced into 4 cm pieces**
1 large onion, chopped
3 large carrots, chopped
2 celery sticks, chopped
½ cup (125 ml) white wine
1 rosemary sprig
¼ cup chopped flat-leaf parsley
¼ cup chopped basil,
** plus extra leaves to serve**
2 teaspoons dried oregano
2 bay leaves
3 garlic cloves, grated
400 g can diced tomatoes
2 tablespoons tomato paste
400 g can butter beans,
** drained and rinsed**
steamed green beans, to serve

1 Place pork, onion, carrot, celery, wine, rosemary, parsley, basil, oregano, bay leaves, garlic, tomato and tomato paste in a 4.5 litre (18-cup) capacity slow-cooker. Cook covered on high for 2 hours. Add butter beans and cook for 15–20 minutes.

2 Serve with extra basil scattered over the top and a side of steamed green beans.

Easy tray bakes

I love meals that can be cooked all on one tray. They are so quick to put together, then everything goes in the oven while you relax. Plus, there's minimal washing up!

Turn the page for recipes >

HALOUMI & CHICKPEA TRAY BAKE

MEDITERRANEAN LAMB TRAY BAKE

MAPLE
MUSTARD PORK
& APPLE TRAY
BAKE

EASY SALMON
TRAY BAKE

Haloumi & chickpea tray bake

serves 4   prep 20 min   cook 45 min

 SmartPoints value per serve

Haloumi is a staple in our house. It is especially delicious in this colourful, vegie-packed Mediterranean-inspired midweek meal.

1 zucchini, sliced into rounds
½ red capsicum, sliced
½ yellow capsicum, sliced
1 red onion, sliced
2 carrots, cut into batons
250 g button or Swiss brown mushrooms, sliced
1 small eggplant, diced
400 g can chickpeas, drained and rinsed

4 garlic cloves, crushed
1 teaspoon dried chilli flakes
2 teaspoons dried Italian mixed herbs
1 teaspoon mild paprika
2 teaspoons olive oil
200 g haloumi cheese, cut into 1 cm thick slices
250 g cherry tomatoes
¼ cup flat-leaf parsley leaves

1 Preheat oven to 180°C. Combine zucchini, capsicum, onion, carrot, mushroom, eggplant and chickpeas in a large bowl. Add garlic, chilli flakes, dried herbs, paprika and oil and toss to combine.

2 Transfer vegetables to a baking tray. Cover dish with foil and bake for 35–40 minutes or until vegetables are tender.

3 Preheat grill to high. Season haloumi with black pepper. Add haloumi and tomatoes to dish of vegetables and grill for 5 minutes or until cheese is golden and tomatoes are softened. Serve sprinkled with parsley.

Maple mustard pork & apple tray bake

serves 4   prep 10 min + marinating   cook 45 min

 SmartPoints value per serve

This tray bake tastes incredible, and it makes the house smell amazing! This one is ALL about that marinade over the pork. You can use any meat with this one – chicken works well, too.

¼ cup (60 ml) sugar-free maple syrup
1 tablespoon wholegrain mustard
2 garlic cloves, grated
1½ tablespoons thyme leaves, plus extra to garnish
4 x 125 g pork cutlets, fat trimmed

2 apples, cut into wedges
2 zucchini, thickly sliced
250 g peeled pumpkin, sliced
250 g cherry truss tomatoes
2 teaspoons garlic-infused olive oil

1 Combine maple syrup, mustard, garlic and 1 tablespoon thyme in a shallow dish. Add pork and turn to coat. Cover and place in fridge for 20 minutes.

2 Preheat oven to 180°C. Combine apple, zucchini, pumpkin and tomatoes in a baking tray. Add oil and remaining thyme and toss to evenly coat. Season with salt and pepper.

3 Arrange cutlets over vegetables. Bake for 35–45 minutes or until vegetables are tender and pork is cooked to your liking. Serve with extra thyme leaves.

Anna's tip

Add 100 g potato per person in step 2 for an extra 2 SmartPoints per serve for Green and Blue.

50% Weight Lost | 100% Healthier

Mediterranean lamb tray bake

serves 4   prep 10 min   cook 40 min

4 **4** **4**   **SmartPoints value per serve**

Stuck for a dinner idea? Give this a go. The prep takes 10 minutes and the oven does the rest!

2 zucchini, thickly sliced
1 red capsicum, sliced
1 yellow capsicum, sliced
2 red onions, cut into
**   wedges**
4 carrots, halved
**   lengthways**
8 garlic cloves, 3 chopped,
**   5 left whole, skin on**
2 teaspoons dried oregano
1 teaspoon dried mixed
**   herbs**

zest of 1 lemon, in strips
1 tablespoon chopped
**   rosemary, plus extra**
**   sprigs to serve**
2 tablespoons chopped
**   flat-leaf parsley,**
**   plus extra to serve**
12 x 40 g lean French-
**   trimmed lamb cutlets**

1 Preheat oven to 200°C. Combine zucchini, capsicum, onion and carrot in a baking dish. Sprinkle with chopped garlic, oregano, mixed herbs, lemon zest, rosemary and parsley. Lightly spray with oil and toss to combine. Cover dish with foil and bake for 25 minutes.

2 Arrange lamb cutlets on top of vegetables. Add whole garlic cloves and season with salt and pepper. Bake, uncovered, for 15 minutes or until vegetables are tender and lamb is cooked to your liking. Sprinkle with extra rosemary and parsley.

Easy salmon tray bake

serves 4   prep 10 min   cook 15 min

10 **4** **4**   **SmartPoints value per serve**

If you don't like salmon, try swapping it out with a different fish, or chicken breast or even turkey breast. All of those are much lower in SmartPoints for Green, but if you're after the good healthy fats, then salmon is for you. You can change the veg up too.

2 bunches broccolini
2 bunches asparagus
1 bunch baby carrots,
**   trimmed**
4 x 120 g skinless salmon
**   fillets**
250 g cherry tomatoes,
**   diced**

1½ tablespoons garlic-
**   infused olive oil**
½ cup (40 g) finely grated
**   parmesan cheese**
basil leaves, to garnish
lemon wedges, to serve

1 Preheat oven to 200°C. Line a baking tray with baking paper. Place broccolini, asparagus, carrots, salmon and tomatoes on prepared tray. Drizzle with oil and sprinkle with parmesan.

2 Cover tray with foil and cut two or three slits in top of foil. Bake for 7–8 minutes. Remove foil and bake for a further 3–5 minutes or until vegetables are tender and salmon is cooked to your liking.

3 Serve garnished with basil and lemon wedges for squeezing over.

Swedish meatballs my way

serves 4   prep 10 min   cook 15 min

    SmartPoints value per serve

So I tried my hand at making Swedish meatballs and, although not authentic, man did they taste GOOD! Serve these with mashed potato and veg (or cauliflower rice to keep those SmartPoints low), perfect for soaking up the yummy sauce.

500 g chicken breast mince
½ onion, finely chopped
½ teaspoon ground nutmeg
½ teaspoon allspice
1 small garlic clove, grated
70 ml light thickened cream
  for cooking
½ cup (125 ml) chicken stock
2 teaspoons Dijon mustard
1 teaspoon Worcestershire sauce
chopped flat-leaf parsley,
  to serve

1 Combine mince, onion, nutmeg, allspice and garlic in a medium bowl. Season with salt and pepper. Shape tablespoons of mixture into 28 meatballs.

2 Lightly spray a large non-stick frying pan with oil and heat over medium–high heat. Cook meatballs, turning, for 4–5 minutes or until browned.

3 Meanwhile, combine cream, stock, mustard and Worcestershire sauce in a jug. Add sauce to meatballs and simmer, uncovered, for 10 minutes or until meatballs are cooked through and sauce has thickened. Serve sprinkled with parsley.

Mac & cheese bake with roasted tomatoes

serves 6   prep 15 min   cook 55 min

 SmartPoints value per serve

The one thing I refuse to do is miss out on foods that I love – I just like to make healthier versions of them. For me, mac and cheese is the ultimate comfort food. Topping this off with beautiful ripe roasted tomatoes makes this simple dish a little bit posh.

3 tomatoes, sliced
2 teaspoons dried oregano
250 g dried macaroni
   or other small pasta
1 onion, finely chopped
150 g short-cut bacon,
   fat trimmed, diced
1 garlic clove, grated
100 g grated mozzarella cheese
⅓ cup (25 g) grated
   parmesan cheese
2 eggs, lightly beaten
100 g 99% fat-free plain yoghurt
oregano leaves, to garnish

1   Preheat oven to 180°C. Line a baking tray with baking paper. Place tomato slices on prepared tray, sprinkle with dried oregano and season with salt and pepper. Bake for 20 minutes.

2   Meanwhile, cook pasta in a large saucepan of boiling salted water, following packet instructions, or until just tender. Drain. Set aside to cool slightly.

3   Heat a medium non-stick frying pan over medium–high heat. Cook onion and bacon, stirring, for 5–6 minutes or until golden. Add garlic and cook, stirring, for 1–2 minutes or until bacon is crisp. Cool.

4   Combine cooked pasta, mozzarella, 2 tablespoons parmesan, eggs and yoghurt in a large bowl. Season with salt and pepper. Stir in cooled bacon mixture.

5   Transfer mixture into a 2.5 litre (10-cup) capacity baking dish. Top with roasted tomatoes and sprinkle with remaining parmesan. Bake for 25–30 minutes or until golden. Serve sprinkled with oregano.

Anna's tip

If you use wholemeal pasta then this recipe is 3 SmartPoints on Purple.

50% **Weight Lost** | 100% **Healthier**

Mediterranean sausage & vegetable bake

serves 4   prep 15 min   cook 40 min

6 6 5   SmartPoints value per serve

This easy tray bake is so quick to put together, it's a perfect choice for last-minute dinner guests. There's a lovely burst of flavour in every single bite. Enjoy!

450 g extra-lean beef sausages
1 zucchini, chopped
2 carrots, chopped
250 g cherry tomatoes
300 g butternut pumpkin,
   cut into thin wedges
6 x 40 g baby (chat) potatoes,
   halved
1 red capsicum, chopped
1 large red onion, chopped
3 garlic cloves, halved
2 teaspoons Tuscan seasoning
⅓ cup (80 ml) chicken stock
basil leaves, to serve

1 Preheat oven to 180°C. Arrange sausages, zucchini, carrot, tomatoes, pumpkin, potato, capsicum, onion and garlic in a large baking dish. Sprinkle over Tuscan seasoning and drizzle over stock.

2 Cover dish with foil and bake for 30 minutes. Remove foil and bake for 5–10 minutes or until golden. Serve sprinkled with basil.

50% **Weight Lost** | 100% **Healthier**

Sweet & sour chicken

serves 4   prep 10 min   cook 15 min

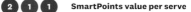 **SmartPoints value per serve**

The regular version of this classic Chinese dish will cost you 10 SmartPoints! With NO rice. Ahhhh, I'll take my version, please! What's more, making this recipe is quicker than ordering in. Feel free to add steamed rice for extra SmartPoints.

2 teaspoons olive oil

1 large red onion, chopped

1 yellow capsicum, chopped

1 red capsicum, chopped

1 orange or green capsicum, chopped

500 g skinless chicken breasts, diced into 2 cm pieces

2 garlic cloves, finely grated

2 tablespoons finely grated ginger

2 tablespoons soy sauce

2 tablespoons light sweet chilli sauce

2 tablespoons white wine vinegar

400 g can pineapple pieces in natural juice, drained

1   Heat oil in a large non-stick frying pan over medium–high heat. Cook onion and capsicum, stirring, for 5–6 minutes or until softened. Add chicken, garlic and ginger and cook, stirring, for 3–4 minutes or until chicken is browned.

2   Add soy sauce, sweet chilli sauce and vinegar, and bring to the boil. Add pineapple and cook, stirring, for 1–2 minutes or until pineapple has warmed through. Season with salt and pepper. Serve.

Bacon, cheese & corn filo tarts

serves 6   prep 15 min   cook 30 min

  SmartPoints value per serve

There's something special about filo pastry – I think it can turn a simple dish into a magical one. My mother raves about these and says they're the best tarts she's ever eaten. She likes the fact that they are so light and yet filled with cheesy goodness. Give them a go!

6 sheets filo pastry

12 eggs

4 corn cobs, kernels removed

2 small leeks, thinly sliced

2 tablespoons chopped herbs (such as parsley, basil or thyme), plus extra to garnish

100 g short-cut bacon, fat trimmed, diced

1 bunch asparagus

½ cup (60 g) grated reduced-fat cheddar cheese

1 tablespoon finely grated parmesan cheese

1 Preheat oven to 180°C. Lightly spray two 11 cm x 34 cm fluted tart tins with removable bases with oil. Line each tin with 3 sheets of filo, spraying lightly between each layer.

2 Whisk eggs in a large bowl until well combined. Add corn, herbs and bacon and stir to combine. Season with salt and pepper. Divide mixture evenly between prepared pastry cases. Top one tart with asparagus and the other with leek. Sprinkle both with cheddar and parmesan.

3 Bake for 25–30 minutes or until golden and set. Set tins aside on a wire rack for 5 minutes to cool slightly. Remove sides of tins and cut each tart into six slices.

4 Serve sprinkled with extra herbs.

Dinner

Maple, soy & sweet chilli salmon

serves 1   prep 5 min + marinating   cook 15 min

  SmartPoints value per serve

The secret of this special fish dinner is the marinade. It is so easy, yet absolutely delicious. If you're not a fan of salmon, swap it for chicken. The SmartPoints remain the same.

**1 tablespoon sugar-free
  maple syrup**
1 tablespoon soy sauce
**1 tablespoon light sweet
  chilli sauce**
160 g skinless salmon fillet
¼ teaspoon black sesame seeds

1 Combine maple syrup, soy sauce and sweet chilli sauce in a shallow baking dish. Add salmon and turn to coat. Cover and place in fridge for at least an hour or overnight if possible.

2 Preheat oven to 200°C. Line a baking tray with baking paper and place salmon on tray. Cook for 15 minutes or until salmon is golden and cooked to your liking (this will depend on how thick your salmon fillet is).

3 Sprinkle with sesame seeds and serve with steamed veg (see tip).

Anna's tip
Serve with lots of steamed veg, such as carrots, green beans and broccoli.

Chilli garlic prawns

serves 1 prep 10 min cook 30 min

 SmartPoints value per serve

On the table in half an hour, this simple dinner packs an amazing flavour punch.

¼ cup (50 g) brown basmati rice
150 g cooked prawns, peeled
**   and deveined**
1 garlic clove, grated
½ teaspoon dried chilli flakes
½ teaspoon Tuscan seasoning
lemon wedges, to serve

1   Cook rice following packet instructions. Set aside.

2   Meanwhile, lightly spray a medium non-stick frying pan with oil and heat over medium–high heat. Cook prawns with garlic, chilli flakes and Tuscan seasoning, stirring, for 1–2 minutes or until prawns are warmed through.

3   Serve prawns with rice and lemon wedges (see tip).

Anna's tip
I also like to serve this with steamed broccoli and cherry tomatoes.

50% **Weight Lost** | 100% **Healthier**

Old-fashioned tuna patties

makes 8   prep 15 min   cook 25 min

3 **2** **1**   **SmartPoints value per serve (1 patty)**

These make for the perfect light dinner, lunch or party food. A spritz of lemon makes these easy patties out-of-this-world good.

240 g Spud Lite or Carisma potatoes, peeled (see tips)
425 g can tuna in spring water, drained and flaked
1 small onion, finely diced
1 egg, lightly beaten
½ cup (70 g) panko breadcrumbs
¼ cup chopped flat-leaf parsley
2 teaspoons Dijon mustard
1 teaspoon Tuscan seasoning
2 teaspoons finely grated lemon zest
1 tablespoon lemon juice

1   Preheat oven to 180°C. Boil, steam or microwave potatoes until tender. Drain and mash. Set aside to cool.

2   Combine cooled potato, tuna, onion, egg, breadcrumbs, parsley, mustard, Tuscan seasoning, zest and juice in a large bowl. Season with salt and pepper. Shape mixture into 8 patties.

3   Lightly spray a large ovenproof non-stick frying pan with oil and heat over medium–high heat. Cook patties for 1–2 minutes each side or until browned. Transfer pan to oven and bake for 8–10 minutes or until cooked through.

Anna's tips

* Spud Lite and Carisma potatoes are available from larger supermarkets.
* Serve with your favourite mash and steamed green veg.

Dinner

Sesame tuna with mango salsa

serves 2   prep 15 min   cook 10 min

  SmartPoints value per serve

Taking my inspiration from sushi, I created this vibrant and light tuna dish. It's perfect for summer, when mangoes are cheap and plentiful. Pairing the sesame-crusted fish with the refreshing salsa brings an amazing mix of flavours and textures.

2 teaspoons black sesame seeds
2 teaspoons white sesame seeds
2 x 125 g tuna steaks
**2 teaspoons garlic-infused
   olive oil**
½ red capsicum, diced
2 baby cucumbers, diced
½ small red onion, diced
1 large mango, diced
2 tablespoons chopped mint
1 teaspoon finely grated lime zest
1 tablespoon lime juice
lime wedges, to serve

1   Combine seeds in a shallow bowl. Coat both sides of tuna with seeds.

2   Heat oil in a large non-stick frying pan over medium heat. Cook tuna for 2–3 minutes each side or until cooked to your liking.

3   Meanwhile, combine capsicum, cucumber, onion, mango, mint, zest and juice in a medium bowl.

4   Serve tuna topped with mango salsa and lime wedges on the side.

50% **Weight Lost** | 100% **Healthier**

Ricotta, pumpkin & spinach strudel

serves 6   prep 20 min   cook 1 hour

  SmartPoints value per serve

Anything wrapped in pastry is always going to be a winning recipe for me, but using my two favourite ingredients for the filling – pumpkin and ricotta – makes it impossible to beat! It looks tricky to make but, honestly, it is very simple, and it looks really impressive when sliced at the table.

**300 g butternut pumpkin,
   diced into cubes**
2 teaspoons Tuscan seasoning
**500 g frozen chopped
   spinach, thawed**
500 g reduced-fat ricotta cheese
¼ cup chopped flat-leaf parsley
**2 tablespoons chopped
   lemon thyme**
1 teaspoon ground nutmeg
6 sheets filo pastry
**2 tablespoons panko
   breadcrumbs**
1 teaspoon black sesame seeds
1 teaspoon white sesame seeds
mixed salad leaves, to serve

1   Preheat oven to 180°C. Line a baking tray with baking paper. Place pumpkin on prepared tray and lightly spray with oil. Sprinkle with Tuscan seasoning and bake for 20 minutes or until golden and tender. Set aside to cool.

2   Squeeze excess water from spinach. Combine spinach, ricotta, parsley, thyme, nutmeg and pumpkin in a large bowl. Season with salt and pepper.

3   Layer filo sheets on a flat surface, spraying lightly with oil between first 3 sheets. Sprinkle breadcrumbs over final layer. Spoon ricotta mixture along one long edge of filo stack leaving a 6 cm border. Fold short ends in, and roll to enclose filling.

4   Place strudel, seam side down, on prepared tray and lightly spray with oil. Sprinkle with sesame seeds and bake for 35–40 minutes or until golden. Stand for 5 minutes before slicing. Serve with salad leaves.

Black bean pasta with chicken & cherry tomato

serves 2   prep 10 min   cook 10 min

 SmartPoints value per serve

I love using non-traditional pasta such as this black bean spaghetti. You get all the flavour without the added SmartPoints, plus you can serve it with your favourite sauce.

200 g Slendier black bean spaghetti
2 teaspoons garlic-infused olive oil
300 g skinless chicken breasts
20 cherry tomatoes, halved
pinch dried chilli flakes (optional)
½ cup flat-leaf parsley, chopped

1 Cook pasta in a large saucepan of boiling salted water following packet instructions. Drain.

2 Meanwhile, heat oil in a medium non-stick frying pan over medium–high heat. Cook chicken for 5 minutes each side or until golden and cooked through. Transfer to a board and thinly slice.

3 Return frying pan to medium heat. Add tomato, sliced chicken, chilli flakes (if using), and pasta and cook, stirring, for 1–2 minutes or until heated through. Serve sprinkled with parsley.

50% **Weight Lost** | 100% **Healthier**

Quiche taco boats

serves 4   prep 10 min   cook 20 min

  SmartPoints value per serve

Here's a simple idea. Take a soft taco shell and turn it into a cheat's quiche. It can be filled with whatever you have in your fridge. This also works well as a portable meal as well as a main dish.

4 eggs
½ cup (60 g) grated
**   mozzarella cheese**
80 g lean shaved leg ham, diced
1 onion, finely diced
½ teaspoon Italian seasoning
4 x 44 g soft taco shells
15 baby asparagus tips

1   Preheat oven to 180°C. Line a baking tray with baking paper.

2   Whisk eggs and 2 tablespoons water in a large bowl until well combined. Add mozzarella, ham, onion and Italian seasoning. Divide egg mixture between taco shells. Top each with asparagus.

3   Place shells on prepared tray and bake for 20 minutes or until golden and set.

Dinner

Baked barramundi in white wine with vegetables

serves 4   prep 15 min   cook 50 min

   SmartPoints value per serve

Tray bakes are my favourite way of cooking mid-week, because they take so little time and effort but they still capture all the flavour that goes into a really delicious meal. See pages 146–147 for more ideas. In this recipe, adding the fish towards the end of the cooking time keeps it moist and succulent.

4 x 40 g baby (chat) potatoes, halved
4 carrots, cut into thirds
1 large red onion, cut into wedges
4 garlic cloves
2 tablespoon baby capers, rinsed and drained
60 g pitted black olives
250 g cherry truss tomatoes
12 thyme sprigs
150 ml dry white wine
4 x 200 g skinless barramundi fillets
1 tablespoon Tuscan seasoning

1   Preheat oven to 180°C. Combine potatoes, carrots and onion in a large baking tray. Smash garlic with the back of a knife, tear each clove in half and add to tray. Scatter capers, olives, tomatoes and 6 thyme sprigs over vegetables. Drizzle over the white wine. Cover dish with foil, cut 2–3 small slits in foil and bake for 30 minutes.

2   Sprinkle fish with Tuscan seasoning. Remove foil and arrange fish and remaining thyme sprigs on top of vegetables. Bake, uncovered, for 15–20 minutes or until fish is cooked through. Serve.

50% **Weight Lost** | 100% **Healthier**

Sweets

Baking has always been a big part of
my life, and it still is. I've learned that
making smart swaps doesn't mean
having to compromise on taste –
sometimes it even transforms
the original treat into something
more delicious.

Chocolate mousse

serves 1   prep 5 min

6 **3** **3**   **SmartPoints value per serve**

My version of chocolate mousse requires no chilling time and is fluffy, delicious and, best of all, guilt free.

¾ cup (180 g) 99% fat-free plain yoghurt
20 g sugar-free drinking chocolate
2 teaspoons sugar-free maple syrup (see tip)
5 g milk chocolate chips
sliced strawberries and mint leaves (optional), to garnish

1   Whisk yoghurt, drinking chocolate and maple syrup in a small bowl for 1–2 minutes or until light and fluffy. Spoon into a serving glass.

2   Serve topped with chocolate chips, strawberries and mint leaves if you like.

Anna's tip
You can swap the sugar-free maple syrup with pure maple syrup. Check the SmartPoints in your WW app.

Apple, raspberry & white chocolate muffins

makes 12   prep 10 min   cook 30 min

4 3 3   SmartPoints value per serve

Raspberry and white chocolate: a marriage made in muffin heaven. These are so soft and light, and I'm sure they'll become a favourite in your house just as they have in mine.

½ cup (125 ml) no-added-sugar
   apple puree
⅓ cup (75 g) caster sugar
2 eggs
½ cup (120 g) 99% fat-free
   plain yoghurt
1 teaspoon ground cinnamon
1 cup (150 g) self-raising
   flour, sifted
120 g raspberries
1 tablespoon white
   chocolate chips

1 Preheat oven to 160°C. Whisk apple puree and sugar in a large bowl until slightly pale. Add eggs one at a time, whisking well after each addition. Whisk in yoghurt and cinnamon. Add flour and stir until just combined. Gently fold in raspberries.

2 Divide mixture among a 12-hole (½ cup/125 ml) capacity silicone muffin mould and top with white chocolate chips. Bake for 25–30 minutes or until a skewer inserted into the centre of a muffin comes out clean. Set muffins aside in mould for 5 minutes before turning out onto a wire rack to cool.

Anna's tip
Alternatively, you can make 24 (1 tablespoon capacity) mini muffins. Bake at 170°C for 20 minutes.

Lemon & raspberry cheesecakes

makes 12   prep 10 min + chilling   cook 25 min

 SmartPoints value per serve

I make mini cheesecakes for a mid-week treat as they are perfectly portion-controlled. I love to decorate each one with a teaspoon of yoghurt, a couple of raspberries and a chocolate chip.

240 g reduced-fat fresh ricotta cheese
180 g light cream cheese, softened
1 tablespoon xylitol
1 tablespoon finely grated lemon zest
⅓ cup (80 ml) lemon juice
1 egg
1 teaspoon vanilla bean paste
125 g raspberries
¼ cup (60 g) 99% fat free plain yoghurt
10 g milk chocolate chips

Base
100 g sugar-free Maria biscuits
1 tablespoon xylitol
80 g reduced-fat oil spread, melted

1 Preheat oven to 160°C. Line 12 holes of a (⅓ cup/80 ml capacity) muffin tin with paper cases.

2 To make base, process biscuits and xylitol in a food processor until crumbs form. Transfer to a medium bowl. Add melted spread and stir to combine. Divide biscuit mixture between paper cases and press with a teaspoon to form a base. Refrigerate for 10 minutes or until firm.

3 Clean out processor and process ricotta and cream cheese until smooth. Add xylitol, zest, juice, egg and vanilla and process again until well combined. Divide cheese mixture among muffin holes and smooth surfaces.

4 Bake for 20–25 minutes or until just set. Transfer to a wire rack to completely cool. Refrigerate for at least 2–3 hours or until chilled.

5 Serve topped with yoghurt, raspberries and chocolate chips.

Spiced fruit crumble

serves 6   prep 15 min   cook 1 hour

 SmartPoints value per serve

The best thing about crumbles is that the fruit can be changed to your liking, and with the seasons. If you can't get frozen raspberries, swap them for frozen cherries or cranberries. The mixed spice with this fruit combination just sings with delicious sweet/sour notes.

200 g peeled and chopped pink lady apples
200 g peeled and chopped pears
1 cup (150 g) fresh pineapple, chopped
1 cup (140 g) raspberries
2 teaspoons finely grated orange zest
1 teaspoon mixed spice
1 teaspoon vanilla extract

Crumble
1½ tablespoons shredded coconut
30 g plain flour
75 g rolled oats
½ teaspoon ground cinnamon
1 tablespoon butter
1 tablespoon pure maple syrup

1 Preheat oven to 180°C. Combine apple, pear, pineapple and raspberries in a large bowl. Add zest, mixed spice and vanilla, and stir to combine.

2 Place fruit mixture in a 22 cm x 16 cm baking dish. Cover with foil and bake for 45 minutes or until fruit is tender.

3 Meanwhile, combine coconut, flour, oats, cinnamon and a pinch of salt in a small bowl. Add butter and maple syrup and rub with fingertips until coarse crumbs.

4 Once fruit is tender, sprinkle crumble mixture over fruit. Bake, uncovered, for 10–15 minutes or until golden.

Banoffee trifles

makes 4 **prep 10 min + chilling**

 SmartPoints value per serve

Dessert pairings don't get much better than banana and caramel ... until you add Malibu liqueur! The coconut takes this twist on banoffee pie to a new level of deliciousness.

4 large bananas, sliced
2 tablespoons Malibu liqueur
80 g plain sponge cake, diced
160 ml Natvia salty
caramel topping
1 cup (240 g) 99% fat-free
plain yoghurt
⅔ cup (160 g) reduced-fat
custard

1 Combine banana and Malibu in a large bowl.

2 Layer sponge, banana mixture, caramel topping, yoghurt and custard in four 250 ml capacity serving glasses.

3 Cover and refrigerate until ready to serve (see tip).

Anna's tip

Dust serving glasses with 1 teaspoon sugar-free drinking chocolate before serving to decorate.

50% **Weight Lost** | 100% **Healthier**

Vanilla yoghurt pannacotta with raspberries

serves 6   prep 15 min + chilling   cook 5 min

 SmartPoints value per serve

Pannacotta is one of my all-time favourite desserts, but the traditional version is really high in SmartPoints. By using yoghurt and almond milk in this recipe, you can still enjoy that creamy texture and slight wobble without using all your SmartPoints.

1 tablespoon powdered gelatine

2 cups (500 ml) unsweetened almond milk

2 tablespoons pure maple syrup

2 teaspoons vanilla bean paste

2 cups (480 g) 99% fat-free plain yoghurt

250 g raspberries, to serve

1   Place ¼ cup (60 ml) boiling water in a small bowl. Sprinkle gelatine over water and whisk until dissolved. Set aside.

2   Place 1 cup (250 ml) almond milk, maple syrup and vanilla in a small saucepan over medium heat until warm – do not boil. Whisk in gelatine mixture.

3   Combine remaining milk and yoghurt in a large bowl. Gradually whisk in warm milk mixture. Divide mixture among six (⅔ cup/160 ml capacity) serving glasses. Cover and refrigerate for 4 hours or until set. Serve topped with raspberries.

Date, coffee & walnut cake

makes 12   prep 15 min   cook 35 min

3 **3** **3**   **SmartPoints value per serve**

Classic walnut and coffee cake can be so high in SmartPoints, so I made up my mind to create a healthier version. This one has all the flavour without breaking the SmartPoints budget.

250 g self-raising flour
2 eggs, lightly beaten
100 ml espresso coffee
1 teaspoon vanilla essence
½ cup (110 g) apple,
** coarsely chopped**
40 g walnuts, chopped,
** 1 tablespoon reserved**
** to decorate**

Salted date caramel
180 g pitted medjool dates
2 teaspoons sea salt

1 To make the salted date caramel, combine dates, ½ cup (125 ml) hot water and sea salt in a food processor and stand for 10 minutes or until softened. Process until smooth and creamy.

2 Preheat oven to 180°C. Sift flour into a large bowl. Add eggs, coffee, ½ cup (140 g) salted date caramel (see tip), vanilla, apple, walnuts and a pinch of salt, and stir until well combined.

3 Spoon mixture into a silicone loaf tin or line the base and sides of a 22 cm x 12 cm loaf tin with baking paper. Decorate with the reserved walnuts. Bake for 30–35 minutes or until a skewer inserted into the centre comes out clean. Set aside in pan for 5 minutes before transferring to a wire rack to cool.

Anna's tip

The salted date caramel recipe makes 1 cup (280 g). Spoon leftovers into a sterilised jar and store in the fridge for up to 3 months. It is delicious on toast, with fruit salad and yoghurt, or over ice cream. Plus it's 0 SmartPoints per teaspoon.

Sweets

Honey, ricotta & date rolls

makes 16   prep 15 min   cook 15 min

 SmartPoints value per roll

Crunchy, sweet-filled filo pastries make a wonderful treat to take to a family gathering, or just to enjoy for afternoon or morning tea. These are best eaten on the day they are made.

270 g reduced-fat fresh ricotta cheese
2½ teaspoons honey
½ teaspoon ground cinnamon, plus extra to sprinkle
1 teaspoon vanilla essence
60 g pitted medjool dates, chopped
25 g pistachio nut kernels, chopped
6 sheets filo pastry
½ teaspoon pure icing sugar

1 Preheat oven to 180°C. Line a baking tray with baking paper. Combine ricotta, honey, cinnamon, vanilla, dates, pistachios and a pinch of salt in a medium bowl.

2 Lay 1 filo sheet on a flat surface and lightly spray with oil. Repeat with 2 more sheets of filo to make a stack. Repeat with remaining filo sheets to make 2 filo stacks. Cut each stack into eight 10 x 14 cm rectangles.

3 Place 1 tablespoon ricotta mixture in the centre of each rectangle. Roll up like a spring roll and place on tray. Bake for 15 minutes or until golden.

4 Sift icing sugar over the top and sprinkle with cinnamon just before serving.

50% **Weight Lost** | 100% **Healthier**

Apple & rhubarb tea cake

serves 16   prep 15 min   cook 45 min

 SmartPoints value per serve

This gorgeous show-stopping cake has such a light, moist texture, it is just a delight to serve and enjoy at any time. The crunch of the demerara sugar on top makes it extra special, so be sure to not skip that ingredient.

225 g self-raising flour
1 teaspoon baking powder
1 teaspoon ground cinnamon
½ teaspoon salt
½ cup (110 g) golden or white caster sugar
1 tablespoon finely grated orange zest
2 teaspoons finely grated lemon zest
1 egg, lightly beaten
1 cup (250 ml) pure cream
1 teaspoon vanilla essence
225 g pink lady apple, peeled and chopped
225 g rhubarb, chopped
1 tablespoon demerara sugar

1 Preheat oven to 180°C. Lightly spray a 25 cm round springform tin with oil and line base and side with baking paper.

2 Reserve 1 tablespoon flour. Sift remaining flour, baking powder, cinnamon and salt into a large bowl. Stir through caster sugar, orange and lemon zest. Whisk egg, cream and vanilla in a jug until well combined.

3 Reserve 1 tablespoon each of apple and rhubarb. Add half the cream mixture to flour mixture and gently fold to combine. Stir in half the remaining apple and rhubarb, then fold in remaining cream mixture, apple and rhubarb. Combine reserved flour, apple and rhubarb in a small bowl.

4 Pour batter into prepared tin and smooth surface with a spatula. Scatter top with reserved apple and rhubarb mixture and sprinkle with demerara sugar. Bake for 40–45 minutes or until a skewer inserted into the centre comes out clean. Set cake aside in tin to cool for 10 minutes before turning out onto a wire rack to cool.

50% **Weight Lost** | 100% **Healthier**

Almond & pistachio biscuits

makes 36   prep 20 min + chilling   cook 45 min

 SmartPoints value per piece

These wafer-thin Italian biscuits are beautiful with a cup of coffee or tea. They are super easy to make and delicious. They also make a gorgeous homemade gift from the kitchen.

3 egg whites
50 g caster sugar
2 tablespoons finely grated orange zest
1 teaspoon vanilla extract
125 g plain flour
50 g raw almonds
50 g pistachio nut kernels
½ teaspoon ground cinnamon

1 Preheat oven to 180°C. Line a 21 cm x 11 cm loaf tin with baking paper.

2 Using electric beaters, beat egg whites and a pinch of salt until frothy. Gradually add sugar, 1 tablespoon at a time, beating well after each addition until sugar has dissolved and soft peaks form. Beat in zest and vanilla until combined. Gently fold through flour, nuts and cinnamon.

3 Pour mixture into prepared tin. Bake for 35 minutes or until firm and light golden. Set aside in tin to cool for 10 minutes before transferring to a wire rack to cool completely. Wrap in foil and chill in fridge overnight.

4 Preheat oven to 150°C. Using a sharp serrated knife, slice into 2 mm thick slices. Arrange in a single layer on a baking tray. Bake for 10–12 minutes or until crisp. Transfer to a wire rack to cool.

Cinnamon sugar almond macaroons

makes 30   prep 15 min + chilling   cook 30 min

 SmartPoints value per biscuit

These chewy sweet biscuits are a treat for any guests who come to visit. Although bite-sized, they pack a huge hit – enough to satisfy the sweetest tooth.

3 egg whites
1 teaspoon vanilla essence
1 teaspoon ground cinnamon
200 g lite raw reduced-calorie
  sugar
2½ cups (300 g) almond meal
30 raw almonds

1 Using electric beaters, beat egg whites in a large bowl until soft peaks form. Add vanilla and beat to combine. Gently fold in cinnamon, sugar and almond meal. Cover and place in fridge for at least 1 hour or until firm.

2 Preheat oven to 170°C. Line two baking trays with baking paper. Roll tablespoons of mixture into balls. Place on prepared trays 3 cm apart and flatten slightly. Press an almond in the centre of each biscuit.

3 Bake for 25–30 minutes, swapping trays halfway through cooking time, or until light golden. Set aside to cool completely on trays.

Lemon & poppy seed roulade

serves 8   prep 15 min + cooling   cook 10 min

 SmartPoints value per serve

This delightful cake boasts a light lemon-flavoured sponge, crunchy poppy seeds and a velvety smooth filling. Quark has a lovely, thick consistency like Greek yoghurt, and is just a perfect base for adding flavour. Its high protein content is a huge bonus.

3 eggs
50 g caster sugar
30 g plain flour
1½ tablespoons finely grated lemon zest (see tip)
2 teaspoons poppy seeds
250 g 99% fat-free quark cheese
2 teaspoons pure maple syrup
250 g raspberries, halved
½ teaspoon icing sugar
mint leaves, to serve

1 Preheat oven to 200°C. Line a 25 cm x 35 cm Swiss roll tin with baking paper. Using electric beaters beat eggs and sugar in a large bowl for 5–8 minutes or until thick and pale. Sift flour into a small bowl. Fold flour, two-thirds of the zest, poppy seeds and a pinch of salt into egg mixture until just combined.

2 Pour mixture into prepared tin. Bake for 8 minutes or until sponge bounces back lightly when touched.

3 Place a sheet of baking paper the same size as tin on a clean tea towel. Turn hot sponge onto paper and peel away lining paper. Roll sponge (in towel) from one of the short sides. Cool.

4 Meanwhile, combine quark, maple syrup and remaining zest in a medium bowl.

5 Unroll sponge and spread with quark mixture. Top with raspberries, reserving some for decoration. Using paper as a guide, re-roll sponge from the same short side to enclose filling.

6 Decorate with icing sugar, reserved raspberries and mint before serving.

Anna's tip
You will need 3 lemons for this recipe.

Chai-spiced pears in syrup

serves 4   prep 10 min   cook 35 min

 SmartPoints value per serve

My favourite tea is chai: the spices sing of Christmas all year round. In this recipe, the infused liquid is reduced to a delicious syrup and drizzled over the pears. You can certainly leave the fruit whole, or halved, but I quarter them to really infuse all the spice flavours deep into the pears.

4 chai tea bags
2 teaspoons vanilla bean paste
⅓ cup (80 ml) pure maple syrup
1 cinnamon stick
2 star anise
2 teaspoons finely grated orange zest
4 bosc pears, peeled and quartered

1 Combine tea bags, vanilla, maple syrup, cinnamon, star anise, zest and 1 litre (4 cups) water in a large saucepan. Add pears and cook over a medium heat for 20–25 minutes, or until pears are just tender.

2 Transfer pears to a bowl. Increase heat to high and boil poaching liquid until reduced by half. Discard cinnamon, tea bags and star anise.

3 Serve pears drizzled with the syrup.

Anna's tip

If you do not own a fine grater, use a vegetable peeler to zest the orange in strips.

50% **Weight Lost** | 100% **Healthier**

Italian ricotta & rice cake

serves 12 prep 20 min cook 50 min

5 **5** **5** **SmartPoints value per serve**

My grandmother used to make this delectable cake as a family treat. Her recipe included her own Italian pastry and full-fat ricotta. This is my healthier version, which has all the taste of the original.

1 kg reduced-fat fresh ricotta cheese
2 tablespoons finely grated orange zest
4 tablespoons finely grated lemon zest, plus extra to serve
½ teaspoon ground cinnamon, plus extra to serve
2 eggs
150 g lite raw sugar
¼ cup (60 ml) lemon juice
2 cups (320 g) cooked white rice (see tips)
orange segments, to serve

1 Preheat oven to 160°C. Line base and side of a 25 cm round springform tin with baking paper.

2 Process ricotta in a food processor until smooth. Add orange and lemon zest, cinnamon, eggs, sugar and juice and process until smooth. Transfer to a large bowl. Fold through rice.

3 Pour mixture into prepared tin and smooth surface with the back of a spoon. Bake for 50 minutes or until just firm; the cake will still have a slight wobble. Set cake aside in tin to cool completely before removing from tin. Remove side of tin. Slide off paper onto a serving plate. Place in fridge to chill.

4 Serve topped with orange segments, extra lemon zest and cinnamon.

Anna's tips

* **You will need 140 g dried rice to yield 320 g cooked rice. It is best to slightly undercook this rice.**

* **This cake is also delicious eaten at room temperature.**

> **Festive dishes made healthy."**

Let's celebrate

You don't have to miss out on your favourite foods with WW. In this chapter, I show you how to give festive dishes a healthy twist without losing any of the flavour. And keeping dishes visually appealing yet simple brings that amazing WOW factor, while making sure you can enjoy the celebrations, too.

The menu

TO START
Nibble platter

MAINS

Cheat's roast turkey with
Bacon & sage stuffing and Cranberry apple relish
The best honey-glazed ham
Mum's braised prawn-stuffed squid

SIDES

Green beans with orange, hazelnut
& cranberry gremolata
Classic Italian potato salad
Mustard & maple baby carrots

DESSERTS

Fruit mince pie tartlets
My trifle

50% **Weight Lost** | 100% **Healthier**

Nibble platter

I took this to a party with 25 people and it was demolished within minutes! I like to make platters beautiful and also include lots of interesting tastes and textures, and a variety of both sweet and savoury nibbles.

Meat

✱ **250 g 97% fat-free deli ham, sliced**

(1) (1) (1) SmartPoints value per 2 slices

✱ **250 g 97% fat-free deli chicken, sliced**

(1) (1) (1) SmartPoints value per 2 slices

Cheese

✱ **100 g Babybel light cheese**

(2) (2) (2) SmartPoints value per 20 g serve

✱ **125 g Laughing Cow light wedges**

(1) (1) (1) SmartPoints value per wedge

✱ **150 g Jarlsberg light cheese slices**

(1) (1) (1) SmartPoints value per slice

Dips

✱ **1 cup Creamy hummus**
(see page 66)

(0) (0) (0) SmartPoints value per tablespoon

✱ **1 cup Homemade tzatziki**
(see page 67)

(0) (0) (0) SmartPoints value per tablespoon

Something fresh

✱ **1 Lebanese cucumber, sliced**
✱ **6 carrots, peeled and cut into batons**
✱ **6 celery sticks, cut into batons**

(0) (0) (0) SmartPoints value per serve

✱ **250 g raspberries**
✱ **250 g strawberries**
✱ **250 g blackberries**
✱ **1 kg seedless green grapes**

(0) (0) (0) SmartPoints value per serve

Something crunchy

✱ **2 x 75 g packs Waterthins fine wafer crackers**

(1) (1) (1) SmartPoints value per 8 crackers

✱ **100 g pretzels**

(1) (1) (1) SmartPoints value per 10 pretzels

✱ **50 g dry-roasted almonds**

(1) (1) (1) SmartPoints value per 6 almonds

✱ **150 g pickled baby cucumbers**

(0) (0) (0) SmartPoints value for 5 (20 g) cucumbers

Something sweet

✱ **Apple pie bliss balls** (see page 61)

(2) (2) (1) SmartPoints value per ball

✱ **Chocolate brownie bliss balls**
(see page 60)

(1) (1) (1) SmartPoints value per ball

✱ **8 pitted medjool dates**

(0) (0) (0) SmartPoints value per serve

CREAMY HUMMUS DIP
recipe page 66

HOMEMADE TZATZIKI
recipe page 67

BLISS BALLS
recipes pages 60–61

Let's celebrate

CHEAT'S ROAST TURKEY WITH BACON & SAGE STUFFING
pages 204–205

CLASSIC ITALIAN POTATO SALAD
page 203

CRANBERRY APPLE RELISH
page 205

GREEN BEANS WITH ORANGE, HAZELNUT & CRANBERRY GREMOLATA

page 202

MUSTARD & MAPLE BABY CARROTS

page 202

Green beans with orange, hazelnut & cranberry gremolata

serves 4 prep 10 min cook 5 min

2 2 2 SmartPoints value per serve

Absolutely packed with flavour, this gremolata topping goes beautifully with just-tender green beans. Try pairing it with fish, grilled chicken or roast lamb for a festive meal.

400 g baby green beans
¼ cup chopped flat-leaf parsley
2 teaspoons finely grated orange zest
1 garlic clove, grated
2 tablespoons roasted hazelnuts, chopped
2 tablespoons 50%-less-sugar craisins
1 tablespoon orange juice
1 teaspoon olive oil

1 Boil, steam or microwave beans until just tender. Drain and rinse under cold running water. Drain.

2 To make gremolata, combine parsley, zest, garlic, hazelnuts and craisins. Arrange beans on a serving platter. Drizzle with orange juice and olive oil, then sprinkle with the gremolata before serving.

Mustard & maple baby carrots

serves 4 prep 10 min cook 15 min

2 2 2 SmartPoints value per serve

This recipe couldn't be any easier: just whisk, toss and roast – you don't even need to peel the baby carrots!

600 g baby carrots
1 tablespoon pure maple syrup
1½ tablespoons wholegrain mustard
2 teaspoons garlic-infused olive oil
1 tablespoon soy sauce

1 Preheat oven to 180°C. Place carrots in a baking dish. Whisk maple syrup, mustard, oil and soy sauce together in a small jug. Drizzle over carrots and toss to combine.

2 Roast for 35–40 minutes or until golden and tender. Serve.

50% **Weight Lost** | 100% **Healthier**

Classic Italian potato salad

serves 6   prep 15 min   cook 20 min

4 4 2   **SmartPoints value per serve**

My family have been making potato salad this way for generations: scented with herbs and drizzled with a simple vinaigrette. The secret is adding the dressing while the potato is still warm to really infuse all the flavours.

**700 g baby (chat) potatoes,
  quartered or halved**
1 tablespoon salt
**2 tablespoons extra-virgin
  olive oil**
1 tablespoon red wine vinegar
1 tablespoon lemon juice
⅓ cup chopped flat-leaf parsley
2 teaspoons dried oregano
¼ red onion, finely diced

1 Place potatoes in a large saucepan of cold water. Bring to the boil over high heat and add salt. Reduce heat and cook, uncovered, for 20 minutes or until just tender. Drain potatoes and return to pan.

2 Meanwhile, whisk oil, vinegar and juice together in a small jug.

3 Transfer potatoes to a large bowl. Add dressing, parsley, oregano and onion, and toss to combine. Season with salt and pepper. Serve at room temperature.

Cheat's roast turkey

serves 8   prep 5 min   cook 1 hour 30 min

 SmartPoints value per serve

Welcome to my cheat's roast! I don't always have time to do a full-sized turkey –
plus, I would rather concentrate on the stuffing. For me, that is the best part! Perfect.
The cranberry relish fills the house with amazing aromas and is so much better than
store-bought versions.

1 kg frozen turkey breast

1 Defrost turkey in fridge for 24 hours.

2 Preheat oven to 180°C. Place a trivet or roasting rack in a baking dish.
   Place turkey on trivet and add 1 cup (250 ml) water to base of dish. Cover
   with foil and bake for 1 hour 30 minutes or until juices run clear when a
   skewer is inserted into the thickest part of the turkey. Transfer turkey to
   a plate. Cover with foil and set aside to rest for 10 minutes before slicing.

3 Serve with the bacon and sage stuffing and cranberry apple relish opposite.

50% **Weight Lost** | 100% **Healthier**

Bacon & sage stuffing

serves 8 prep 15 min cook 55 min

   SmartPoints value per serve

1 large onion, finely chopped
200 g short-cut bacon, fat trimmed, finely chopped
500 g button mushrooms, diced
3 garlic cloves, grated
1 tablespoon port
2 teaspoons finely grated lemon zest
1 tablespoon thyme leaves, plus extra to serve
⅓ cup chopped flat-leaf parsley
¼ cup sage leaves, finely chopped
2 cups (140 g) chunky breadcrumbs from stale sourdough
2 eggs, lightly beaten

1 Preheat oven to 180°C. Heat a large non-stick frying pan over medium heat. Cook onion and bacon for 5 minutes or until onion is golden. Add mushrooms, stirring, for 6–7 minutes or until tender. Add garlic and port, and cook for 5 minutes or until liquid has evaporated. Transfer mixture to a large bowl.

2 Add zest, thyme, parsley and sage, and season with salt and pepper. Add breadcrumbs and egg, and stir to combine.

3 Lightly spray a large sheet of foil with oil. Place mixture on foil close to one of the long edges and shape into a 32 cm x 7 cm log. Roll foil away from you over the mixture, shaping as you roll. Tuck ends under and place roll on baking tray.

4 Roast with turkey for last 30–35 minutes or until cooked through. Garnish with extra thyme.

Cranberry apple relish

serves 15 prep 5 min cook 25 min

 **SmartPoints value per serve**

350 g frozen cranberries
2 large pink lady apples (about 300 g), peeled and finely chopped
1 onion, finely chopped
120 g medjool dates, pitted and finely chopped
½ cup (125 ml) freshly squeezed orange juice
2 teaspoons finely grated orange zest
¼ cup (55 g) brown sugar
¼ cup (60 ml) apple cider vinegar
1 teaspoon ground cinnamon
1 teaspoon mixed spice
¼ teaspoon ground cloves

1 Combine all ingredients in a large saucepan. Season with salt and pepper. Bring to the boil over high heat, then reduce heat and simmer, uncovered, for 20–25 minutes or until a relish consistency forms.

Mum's braised prawn-stuffed squid

serves 8   prep 25 min   cook 1 hr 30 min

 SmartPoints value per serve

My mum makes this beautiful dish on special occasions, including every Christmas, as it's one of my favourite ways to eat squid. The slow braise makes the squid so very tender and enhances the flavour of the filling.

3 x 400 g cans diced tomatoes
1 teaspoon garlic-infused or extra-virgin olive oil
1 onion, finely chopped
2 garlic cloves, grated
300 g peeled green prawns
150 g firm white fish fillet
1 cup (140 g) panko breadcrumbs
¼ cup (20 g) finely grated parmesan cheese
¼ cup chopped basil
¼ cup chopped flat-leaf parsley
1 egg
8 x 150 g squid tubes, cleaned

1 Process tomatoes in a food processor or blender until smooth. Heat oil in a large saucepan over medium heat. Cook onion, stirring, for 5 minutes or until softened. Add garlic and cook, stirring, for 30 seconds or until fragrant. Add pureed tomato and bring to the boil. Reduce heat and simmer, partially covered, for 15–20 minutes or until reduced.

2 Meanwhile, clean out processor. Process prawns and fish until chunky. Add breadcrumbs, parmesan, basil, parsley and egg. Season with salt and pepper and process until just combined.

3 Score the outside of the stuffed squid to allow expansion while cooking. Stuff prawn mixture into squid tubes and secure with toothpicks. Add stuffed squid to the tomato sauce and gently simmer, covered, for 1 hour or until squid is tender.

50% **Weight Lost** | 100% **Healthier**

Fruit mince pie tartlets

makes 12   prep 10 min   cook 30 min

 SmartPoints value per tartlet

My husband LOVES fruit mince pies, so I made it my mission to make homemade fruit mince. Most people enjoy a mince tart at Christmas time, but they are often so heavy with pastry that you can't taste the actual filling. Here's my solution!

12 x 6 g wonton wrappers
2 teaspoons icing sugar

My fruit mince
2 large pink lady apples, grated
12 medjool dates, pitted
   and chopped
50 g raisins
50 g currants
¼ teaspoon mixed spice
½ teaspoon ground cinnamon
2 tablespoons sugar-free
   maple syrup
2 teaspoons finely grated
   orange zest
¼ cup (60 ml) orange juice

1 To make the fruit mince, combine all fruit mince ingredients with ½ cup (125 ml) water in a saucepan and cook over low heat for 15 minutes or liquid has evaporated and dried fruit is plump. You'll need 300 g for this recipe. Set the rest aside to cool completely before storing in a sterilised jar.

2 Preheat oven to 180°C. Line a 12-hole (2 tablespoon capacity) mini-muffin tin with wonton wrappers. Lightly spray wrappers with oil.

3 Divide 300 g of the fruit mince evenly among lined muffin holes. Bake for 10–15 minutes or until golden. Serve dusted with icing sugar.

The best honey-glazed ham

serves 26 prep 10 min + marinating cook 1 hour

 SmartPoints value per serve

My mother-in-law makes THE BEST honey-glazed ham. It has always been the highlight of Christmas with the family, so I'm excited to share my version of it, which I have made WW-friendly. I love serving it with my cranberry apple relish on page 205 and steamed greens. Thanks, Mum!

1 x 4 kg leg ham, partially boned
¼ cup (90 g) honey
2 teaspoons French mustard
2 tablespoons dry sherry
2 tablespoons soy sauce
2 tablespoons brown sugar
½ teaspoon dried chilli flakes
rosemary and thyme sprigs,
**   to garnish**

1 Using a sharp knife, cut a zig-zag pattern around the shank (around 10 cm from end) of ham. Remove and discard rind and most of the fat so only a thin layer remains. Score flesh/fat diagonally at 2 cm intervals to form a diamond pattern.

2 Combine honey, mustard, sherry, soy sauce, sugar and chilli flakes.

3 Place ham in a disposable foil tray. Pour over marinade. Cover and place in fridge to marinate, spooning marinade over ham occasionally, for 48 hours.

4 Preheat oven to 200°C. Cover tray with foil and bake for 50 minutes. Remove foil and bake for 10 minutes or until golden.

5 Garnish with herbs, then slice and serve.

My trifle

serves 12 prep 20 min + chilling

  SmartPoints value per serve

What a grand-looking trifle for the centre of the table at any celebration! It may not have the cake element, but you certainly won't miss it. It's a crowd-pleaser without all the SmartPoints attached.

**2 x 9 g packets lite
  strawberry jelly**
125 g raspberries
250 g strawberries, sliced
2 x 9 g packets lite lime jelly
400 g low-fat vanilla custard
700 g 99% fat-free plain yoghurt
375 g mixed berries
15 dry-roasted almonds, chopped
mint leaves, to garnish

1 Place strawberry jelly crystals in a large heatproof bowl or dish. Add 2 cups (500 ml) boiling water and whisk until dissolved. Add 2 cups (500 ml) cold water (see tips) and stir to combine.

2 Place raspberries and strawberries around the base of a 3-litre capacity serving bowl. Carefully pour jelly over fruit. Place in fridge for 3–4 hours or until set.

3 Place lime jelly crystals in a large heatproof bowl or dish. Add 2 cups (500 ml) boiling water and whisk until dissolved. Add 2 cups (500 ml) cold water and stir to combine. Carefully pour over strawberry jelly. Return to fridge for 3–4 hours or until set.

4 Top lime jelly with a layer of custard. Place yoghurt in a piping bag and carefully pipe over custard (see tips), refilling piping bag as necessary. Serve topped with mixed berries (see tips) and chopped almonds, with a few mint leaves to garnish.

Anna's tips
* Piping the yoghurt over the custard layer prevents the two mixing with each other.
* Use cold water from the fridge to help set the jelly layers faster.
* Add the fruit just before serving so it doesn't sink into the yoghurt layer.

Thanks

I never thought I would write a cookbook, but here I am: an everyday mum and wife who has done just that. But it would never have come to fruition without the amazing team behind me.

As I took those first steps on my weight-loss journey, I could never have imagined how dramatically my life would change. I never thought that I would end up sharing my story with so many people. And as for writing a cookbook, well, I thought only famous people did that!

For this to become possible, I owe so many thanks to so many amazing people who have believed in me along the way, both professionally and personally.

My gratitude to the incredible team at Pan Macmillan, Ariane Durkin, Naomi van Groll, Charlotte Ree and especially Ingrid Ohlsson, for seeing something in me, my story and my recipes that could potentially help so many other people wanting to change their own lifestyle. I am truly thankful, because without that belief none of this could have happened.

To the magical team at WW that I have worked so closely with, I have so much respect for the dedication and hard work you have all put into this project to make it come alive. To Trusha Madhoo, Jade Leung, Jasmine Loxton, Michelle Celander and my special friend and mentor, Lucy Kelly, a huge thank you for your guidance and for believing in me, my work and my purpose, and sharing my vision.

To my agent, Melanie Ostell, who continues to believe that I have made a difference to people's lives, and has helped me understand that, and continuously supported me every step of the way.

My endless thanks to my ever-supportive husband, Rodney. You are my best friend. You have been by my side at my heaviest, weakest, strongest and healthiest, and everything in between. I wouldn't be where I am and who I am without your constant love, belief and faith in me.

Thank you for loving me the way you do. You are the kindest and gentlest soul I have ever met and those who know you can attest to that. I am indeed the luckiest woman in the world, because you make me feel like the only woman in your world.

I come from a long line of strong women; however, I didn't think I was one of them. How little I knew myself. So to all the women in my life who have influenced, loved, taught, nurtured and encouraged me through this whole journey of life, I thank you. In one way or another you've all played an important part in the woman I have become today – especially my amazing mum and my beautiful nonna, who I speak about so often.

My darling sister, Christina. While you were here, you made this world a better place; since you've been gone, you made me a better person. I wish you were here every day, but I feel your love surrounding us all, always. I hope I make you proud.

For my son, Ethan. You came into my world and showed me what real love is. I am so privileged and proud to be your mum. You are my inspiration and you gave me the courage I needed to make these changes. You made me brave, and you continue to do so every day. I love you with all my heart.

Thank you to my amazing community: my coaches, my mum and dad, my family and my friends who have supported me for all these years.

And finally, to you, the reader: this book is for you. I hope my story will motivate, support and encourage you, and that it inspires you to believe that change CAN happen: it just has to start with you.

Conversion chart

Measuring cups and spoons may vary slightly from one country to another, but the difference is generally not enough to affect a recipe. All cup and spoon measures are level.

One Australian metric measuring cup holds 250 ml (8 fl oz), one Australian tablespoon holds 20 ml (4 teaspoons) and one Australian metric teaspoon holds 5 ml. North America, New Zealand and the UK use a 15 ml (3 teaspoon) tablespoon.

LENGTH	
Metric	Imperial
3 mm	⅛ inch
6 mm	¼ inch
1 cm	½ inch
2.5 cm	1 inch
5 cm	2 inches
18 cm	7 inches
20 cm	8 inches
23 cm	9 inches
25 cm	10 inches
30 cm	12 inches

LIQUID MEASURES	
One American pint	One Imperial pint
500 ml (16 fl oz)	600 ml (20 fl oz)

cup	Metric	Imperial
⅛ cup	30 ml	1 fl oz
¼ cup	60 ml	2 fl oz
⅓ cup	80 ml	2½ fl oz
½ cup	125 ml	4 fl oz
⅔ cup	160 ml	5 fl oz
¾ cup	180 ml	6 fl oz
1 cup	250 ml	8 fl oz
2 cups	500 ml	16 fl oz
2¼ cups	560 ml	20 fl oz
4 cups	1 litre	32 fl oz

50% **Weight Lost** | 100% **Healthier**

Conversion chart

DRY MEASURES

The most accurate way to measure dry ingredients is to weigh them. However, if using a cup, add the ingredient loosely to the cup and level with a knife; don't compact the ingredient unless the recipe requests 'firmly packed'.

Metric	Imperial
15 g	½ oz
30 g	1 oz
60 g	2 oz
125 g	4 oz (¼ lb)
185 g	6 oz
250 g	8 oz (½ lb)
375 g	12 oz (¾ lb)
500 g	16 oz (1 lb)
1 kg	32 oz (2 lb)

OVEN TEMPERATURES

Celsius	Fahrenheit
100°C	200°F
120°C	250°F
150°C	300°F
160°C	325°F
180°C	350°F
200°C	400°F
220°C	425°F

Celsius	Gas mark
110°C	¼
130°C	½
140°C	1
150°C	2
170°C	3
180°C	4
190°C	5
200°C	6
220°C	7
230°C	8
240°C	9
250°C	10

Index

50% **Weight Lost** | 100% **Healthier**

Index

50% **Weight Lost** | 100% **Healthier**

Index

Index

50% **Weight Lost** | 100% **Healthier**

First published 2020 in Macmillan
by Pan Macmillan Australia Pty Limited
Level 25, 1 Market Street, Sydney, New South Wales
Australia 2000

Photographs Jeremy Simons copyright © Pan Macmillan 2020
Photographs on pages 7, 14, 19, 20 © Anna Van Dyken 2020
Images on pages 10, 27, 197 © Unsplash
Images on pages 1, 5, 14, 19, 20, 27, 68, 92, 106, 138, 146, 147, 159, 164, 178, 204, 205 © Shutterstock

A CIP catalogue record for this book is available from the National Library of Australia: http://
catalogue.nla.gov.au

Design by Northwood Green
Index by Helena Holmgren
Prop and food styling by Vanessa Austin
Cover prop styling by Emma Knowles
Cover food styling by Amber De Florio
Food preparation by Sarah Mayoh
Makeup by Samantha Powell
Colour + reproduction by Splitting Image Colour Studio
Printed in China by Hang Tai Printing Co. Limited